CGP School Classics

Animal Farm

by George Orwell

There's a lot going on in *Animal Farm*, but don't worry — this CGP book will help you understand it in greater depth.

It has the full text plus helpful annotations, a list of key events for quick and easy navigation, and useful Knowledge Organisers to summarise all the key information. Put it all together and you'll be smarter than Boxer trying to learn the alphabet!

How to access your free Online Edition

This book includes a free Online Edition to read on your PC, Mac or tablet. To access it, just go to **cgpbooks.co.uk/extras** and enter this code...

By the way, this code only works for one person. If somebody else has used this book before you, they might have already claimed the Online Edition.

Published by CGP

Editors:
Andy Cashmore
Emma Crighton

With thanks to Gabrielle Richardson and
Bryn Shortland for the proofreading.

With thanks to Jan Greenway for the copyright research.

ISBN: 978 1 78908 948 6
Printed by Bell and Bain Ltd, Glasgow.
Clipart from Corel®

Contents

Introduction

Animal Farm is a short novella, but there's plenty to it. Written in 1943-1944 during the Second World War, and first published in 1945, it tells the story of an animal uprising on a farm in England.

The novella is more than just a farmyard tale though — George Orwell cleverly uses the story of *Animal Farm* to criticise powerful dictatorships and corrupt power. In particular, he's criticising one famous dictatorship: Stalin's rule over the communist Soviet Union.

Orwell was alive during the Russian Revolution and Stalin's rule over Russia, and saw the power and corruption of those in charge. So it's not a *huge* surprise that Orwell wrote such a sharp critique of government and power in this book — especially when you take the rest of his life experiences into account.

The Life of George Orwell

> **1903** — Born in India to a British family
> **1922-27** — Worked as a policeman in Burma
> **1936-39** — Volunteered to fight in the Spanish Civil War
> **1943-44** — *Animal Farm* written
> **1945** — *Animal Farm* published
> **1950** — Died, aged 46

Early Life

Orwell's real name was Eric Arthur Blair. He was born to a middle-class family in India in 1903, but moved to England at a young age.

After school, he became a policeman in Burma, a British colony. He felt ashamed of this role when he realised the Burmese were ruled by the British against their will — this suggests that, many years before *Animal Farm*, he was already aware of the negative impact of powerful rulers.

Return to England

In 1927, Blair moved back to England and took up his famous pen name — George Orwell. He went on to publish lots of books, and was a well-known author by the time he wrote *Animal Farm*.

Outside of writing, Orwell fought in the Spanish Civil War against the right-wing Nationalists. He also worked as a journalist for the BBC during the Second World War. All of this gave him an insight into the political situation of the day, especially the corruption of some powerful governments.

Writing Animal Farm

Orwell wrote *Animal Farm* during the Second World War — between 1943 and 1944. At this time, the United Kingdom and Soviet Union had an alliance against Nazi Germany. As the novella was critical of Stalin and the Soviet Union, lots of publishers rejected it. It wasn't published until August 1945, when tensions between the UK and Soviet Union had begun to grow. Once published, the book proved to be a huge success.

Historical Background

Animal Farm is an allegory for events in Soviet Russia from around 1917-1943 — this means that the novella represents those events.

Key Events
1917 — Tsar overthrown in Russian Revolution
1924 — Lenin dies, leading to a power struggle
1929 — Stalin exiles Trotsky
Early 1930s — Purges (mass executions) and famine
1939 — Outbreak of WWII

The Russian Revolution

Leading up to the revolution, Russia had been ruled by Tsar Nicholas II since 1894. He was a powerful but unpopular leader, and the lower classes suffered under his reign.

Things came to a head in 1917, when the Russian people rioted, forcing the Tsar to give up the throne. The monarchy was later replaced by a Communist government, led by the revolutionary Vladimir Lenin. There are direct parallels between these events and the events in *Animal Farm*: the drunken farmer Jones represents the corrupt Tsar, the beloved leader Old Major represents Lenin, and the rebellion on the farm represents the Russian Revolution.

The Trotsky-Stalin Power Struggle

Lenin led the Communist Party until his death in 1924, at which point there was a power struggle. Leon Trotsky (represented by Snowball in the novella) seemed the obvious choice to take over — he was Lenin's right-hand man and was a gifted leader of the army.

However, it was Joseph Stalin, the Communist Party's General Secretary, who ended up being victorious in the struggle. Stalin (represented by Napoleon in the novella) used his role to increase his control within the government. By 1929, Stalin had seized power and exiled Trotsky.

Stalin's Russia

Stalin took steps to ensure he kept his newly gained power. He removed Trotsky from history books and photos so people would forget him. He also altered photos to show him and Lenin as friends so he was associated with the beloved leader. These actions are reflected in the novella too — Napoleon displays Old Major's skull so he is associated with Old Major's ideals and rewrites history to demonise Snowball.

Sadly, Stalin's Russia was not the one promised by Lenin — instead he created a dictatorship where people lived in fear. Millions of people were killed, some after being tortured into confessing they had betrayed Stalin. This is reflected in the novella by Napoleon's execution of those who confess to working with Snowball.

Despite this state of fear, complete control wasn't simple to attain for Stalin. For example, he faced resistance from the kulaks (rich peasants) who refused to turn their food over to the state. When threatened by Stalin's troops, the kulaks burned their own crops and killed their livestock, which eventually led to a famine in Russia. The hens' refusal to give Napoleon their eggs parallels this moment in Russian history.

Key Themes in *Animal Farm*

Animalism

Animalism is born during Old Major's speech in the first chapter. He sets out its key ideals: humans are bad and animals should be free to benefit from their own labour. However, these idealistic principles don't last — although the name remains, Animalism gradually deteriorates under Napoleon's rule.

The parallels between Animalism and communism are clear — both are about equality, and Animalism can be read as a direct allegory for the failure of communism under Stalin. However, Orwell's aim was not <u>just</u> to criticise Stalin's Russia. The novella can also be read as a broader comment on corrupt leadership, and the dangers of letting those in power have total control.

Education and Social Class

What an animal knows contributes greatly to their social standing — the pigs, who learn to read and write, are accepted as leaders because they're seen as the most intelligent animals. As a result, they're able to shape Animal Farm to their liking. On the other hand, unintelligent animals, such as Boxer, become part of a lower working class — they're easily manipulated by the pigs and unable to stand up to the intelligent ruling class.

Power and Language

The ability to effectively use language brings power on Animal Farm. Squealer's incredibly persuasive language reinforces Napoleon's power, while other animals who are unable to express their feelings through words have no power. Napoleon recognises this and shuts down freedom of speech by attacking opposition (Snowball) and removing the Sunday meetings — he knows if the animals can't speak out against him, it's harder for them to overthrow him.

Propaganda

Perhaps the most powerful tool of control in the novella is propaganda — Squealer uses it to successfully justify the pigs' selfish actions and convince the other animals that things on the farm are good. The animals don't see that they are being misled by Squealer's lies and, worse still, they begin to unintentionally spread propaganda of their own accord. For example, Boxer's maxim "Napoleon is always right" reinforces Napoleon's control over the animals.

Orwell's Writing Techniques

> Orwell really wanted to make it clear how a revolution could easily go bad if corrupt leaders were left unopposed. The techniques he uses present this idea to the reader.

Narrative Style
The narrative voice of *Animal Farm* is detached and matter-of-fact, using simple and unemotional language even when the events being described are horrific or shocking. The effect of this is that readers can build their own opinion of events rather than be influenced by the narrator — in some ways, Orwell's narrative is the exact opposite of the persuasive propaganda displayed in the novella.

Another distinctive aspect of Orwell's narrative style is the use of irony — for example, often the pigs will say one thing to trick the animals, but mean something entirely different. While the animals don't pick up on this, the reader does, emphasising how naive the animals are and how vulnerable they are to manipulation.

Structure
The novella is structured chronologically, showing the rise and fall of Animal Farm over time. The first half of the novella shows the animals believing they are working towards a common goal, but things take a turn in Chapter Five when Napoleon takes charge. Afterwards comes the gradual decline of Animalism, as Napoleon and the pigs undermine each commandment in turn.

The events of the novella are cyclical — the story starts with a drunk, oppressive ruler who treats the animals badly (Jones) and ends in the same way (Napoleon). The repetition of events reflects how history repeated itself in Russia — the peasants suffered under the Tsar, and then under Stalin too.

Key Events

Here are some of the key events in *Animal Farm*:

Chapter One

Mr Jones, of the Manor Farm, had locked the hen-houses for the night, but was too drunk to remember to shut the pop-holes[1]. With the ring of light from his lantern dancing from side to side, he lurched across the yard, kicked off his boots at the back door, drew himself a last glass of beer from the barrel in the scullery, and made his way up to bed, where Mrs Jones was already snoring.

As soon as the light in the bedroom went out there was a stirring and a fluttering all through the farm buildings. Word had gone round during the day that old Major, the prize Middle White boar, had had a strange dream on the previous night and wished to communicate it to the other animals. It had been agreed that they should all meet in the big barn as soon as Mr Jones was safely out of the way. Old Major (so he was always called, though the name under which he had been exhibited was Willingdon Beauty) was so highly regarded on the farm that everyone was quite ready to lose an hour's sleep in order to hear what he had to say.[2]

At one end of the big barn, on a sort of raised platform, Major was already ensconced on his bed of straw, under a lantern which hung from a beam. He was twelve years old and had lately grown rather stout, but he was still a majestic-looking pig, with a wise and benevolent appearance in spite of the fact that his tushes[3] had never been cut. Before long the other animals began to arrive and make themselves comfortable after their different fashions. First came the three dogs, Bluebell, Jessie and Pincher, and then the pigs, who

---

1. pop-holes — holes in a fence or building for animals to pass through.
2. Character: Old Major — *Animal Farm* is an allegory for the Russian Revolution (see p.98-99). Old Major represents Lenin, the leader of the Bolshevik party. Here, Old Major is greatly admired, just as Lenin was by the Bolsheviks.
3. tushes — tusks

settled down in the straw immediately in front of the platform.[1] The hens perched themselves on the window-sills, the pigeons fluttered up to the rafters, the sheep and cows lay down behind the pigs and began to chew the cud. The two cart-horses, Boxer and Clover, came in together, walking very slowly and setting down their vast hairy hoofs with great care lest there should be some small animal concealed in the straw.[2] Clover was a stout motherly mare approaching middle life, who had never quite got her figure back after her fourth foal. Boxer was an enormous beast, nearly eighteen hands high, and as strong as any two ordinary horses put together. A white stripe down his nose gave him a somewhat stupid appearance, and in fact he was not of first-rate intelligence, but he was universally respected for his steadiness of character and tremendous powers of work.[3] After the horses came Muriel, the white goat, and Benjamin, the donkey. Benjamin was the oldest animal on the farm, and the worst tempered. He seldom talked, and when he did it was usually to make some cynical remark — for instance, he would say that God had given him a tail to keep the flies off, but that he would sooner have had no tail and no flies. Alone among the animals on the farm he never laughed. If asked why, he would say that he saw nothing to laugh at. Nevertheless, without openly admitting it, he was devoted to Boxer; the two of them usually spent their Sundays together in the small paddock beyond the orchard, grazing side by side and never speaking.

The two horses had just lain down when a brood of ducklings, which had lost their mother, filed into the barn, cheeping feebly and wandering from side to side to find some place where they would not be trodden on. Clover made a sort of wall round them with her great foreleg, and the ducklings nestled down inside it and promptly fell asleep. At the last moment Mollie, the foolish, pretty white mare

---

1. Theme: Social Class — The pigs get the best position in the barn. This suggests they think they're superior and shows inequality between the animals.

2. Characters: Boxer & Clover — Orwell establishes from the start that both of these characters are compassionate and care about the other animals on the farm.

3. Character: Boxer — Boxer's determination is an asset to the farm. Despite his lack of intelligence, he is "universally respected", showing that hard work is valued on the farm.

who drew Mr Jones's trap, came mincing daintily in, chewing at a lump of sugar. She took a place near the front and began flirting her white mane, hoping to draw attention to the red ribbons it was plaited with. Last of all came the cat, who looked round, as usual, for the warmest place, and finally squeezed herself in between Boxer and Clover; there she purred contentedly throughout Major's speech without listening to a word of what he was saying.

All the animals were now present except Moses, the tame raven, who slept on a perch behind the back door. When Major saw that they had all made themselves comfortable and were waiting attentively, he cleared his throat and began:

"Comrades, you have heard already about the strange dream that I had last night. But I will come to the dream later. I have something else to say first. I do not think, comrades, that I shall be with you for many months longer, and before I die I feel it my duty to pass on to you such wisdom as I have acquired. I have had a long life, I have had much time for thought as I lay alone in my stall, and I think I may say that I understand the nature of life on this earth as well as any animal now living. It is about this that I wish to speak to you.

"Now, comrades, what is the nature of this life of ours? Let us face it: our lives are miserable, laborious and short. We are born, we are given just so much food as will keep the breath in our bodies, and those of us who are capable of it are forced to work to the last atom of our strength; and the very instant that our usefulness has come to an end we are slaughtered with hideous cruelty. No animal in England knows the meaning of happiness or leisure after he is a year old.[1] No animal in England is free. The life of an animal is misery and slavery: that is the plain truth.[2]

"But is this simply part of the order of Nature? Is it because this land of ours is so poor that it cannot afford a decent life to those who dwell upon it? No, comrades, a thousand times no! The soil

---

1. Setting — Although the novel reflects events in Russia, it is set in England. This shows that a corrupt leader could rise in any country in the world.

2. Background & Context — This speech echoes famous socialist Karl Marx's criticisms of capitalism. Marx believed that capitalism was flawed, because rich business-owners profited from the labour of the working classes, who received very little of that profit.

of England is fertile, its climate is good, it is capable of affording food in abundance to an enormously greater number of animals than now inhabit it. This single farm of ours would support a dozen horses, twenty cows, hundreds of sheep — and all of them living in a comfort and a dignity that are now almost beyond our imagining. Why then do we continue in this miserable condition? Because nearly the whole of the produce of our labour is stolen from us by human beings. There, comrades, is the answer to all our problems. It is summed up in a single word — Man. Man is the only real enemy we have. Remove Man from the scene, and the root cause of hunger and overwork is abolished for ever.

"Man is the only creature that consumes without producing. He does not give milk, he does not lay eggs, he is too weak to pull the plough, he cannot run fast enough to catch rabbits. Yet he is lord of all the animals. He sets them to work, he gives back to them the bare minimum that will prevent them from starving, and the rest he keeps for himself. Our labour tills the soil, our dung fertilises it, and yet there is not one of us that owns more than his bare skin. You cows that I see before me, how many thousands of gallons of milk have you given during this last year? And what has happened to that milk which should have been breeding up sturdy calves? Every drop of it has gone down the throats of our enemies. And you hens, how many eggs have you laid in this last year, and how many of those eggs ever hatched into chickens? The rest have all gone to market to bring in money for Jones and his men. And you, Clover, where are those four foals you bore, who should have been the support and pleasure of your old age? Each was sold at a year old — you will never see one of them again. In return for your four confinements and all your labour in the fields, what have you ever had except your bare rations and a stall?[1]

"And even the miserable lives we lead are not allowed to reach their natural span. For myself I do not grumble, for I am one of the lucky ones. I am twelve years old and have had over four hundred children. Such is the natural life of a pig. But no animal escapes the

---

1. Language & Style — Persuasive techniques, such as rhetorical questions, show the injustices the animals have faced. This makes the reader sympathise with them.

cruel knife in the end. You young porkers who are sitting in front of me, every one of you will scream your lives out at the block within a year. To that horror we all must come — cows, pigs, hens, sheep, everyone. Even the horses and the dogs have no better fate. You, Boxer, the very day that those great muscles of yours lose their power, Jones will sell you to the knacker[1], who will cut your throat and boil you down for the foxhounds. As for the dogs, when they grow old and toothless Jones ties a brick round their necks and drowns them in the nearest pond.

"Is it not crystal clear, then, comrades, that all the evils of this life of ours spring from the tyranny of human beings? Only get rid of Man, and the produce of our labour would be our own. Almost overnight we could become rich and free. What then must we do? Why, work night and day, body and soul, for the overthrow of the human race! That is my message to you, comrades: Rebellion! I do not know when that Rebellion will come, it might be in a week or in a hundred years, but I know, as surely as I see this straw beneath my feet, that sooner or later justice will be done. Fix your eyes on that, comrades, throughout the short remainder of your lives! And above all, pass on this message of mine to those who come after you, so that future generations shall carry on the struggle until it is victorious.

"And remember, comrades, your resolution must never falter. No argument must lead you astray. Never listen when they tell you that Man and the animals have a common interest, that the prosperity of the one is the prosperity of the others. It is all lies. Man serves the interests of no creature except himself. And among us animals let there be perfect unity, perfect comradeship in the struggle. All men are enemies. All animals are comrades.[2]"

At this moment there was a tremendous uproar. While Major was speaking four large rats had crept out of their holes and were sitting on their hindquarters, listening to him. The dogs had suddenly caught sight of them, and it was only by a swift dash for their holes

---

1. knacker — a person who disposes of animals, often processing them into animal feed.
2. Key Quote — These two short sentences summarise the fundamentals of Old Major's beliefs. They suggest that humanity is the only enemy the animals need to worry about.

that the rats saved their lives.[1] Major raised his trotter for silence:

"Comrades," he said, "here is a point that must be settled. The wild creatures, such as rats and rabbits—are they our friends or our enemies? Let us put it to the vote. I propose this question to the meeting: Are rats comrades?"

The vote was taken at once, and it was agreed by an overwhelming majority that rats were comrades. There were only four dissentients, the three dogs and the cat, who was afterwards discovered to have voted on both sides.[2] Major continued:

"I have little more to say. I merely repeat, remember always your duty of enmity towards Man and all his ways. Whatever goes upon two legs is an enemy. Whatever goes upon four legs, or has wings, is a friend. And remember also that in fighting against Man, we must not come to resemble him. Even when you have conquered him, do not adopt his vices. No animal must ever live in a house, or sleep in a bed, or wear clothes, or drink alcohol, or smoke tobacco, or touch money, or engage in trade. All the habits of Man are evil. And, above all, no animal must ever tyrannise over his own kind. Weak or strong, clever or simple, we are all brothers. No animal must ever kill any other animal.[3] All animals are equal.[4]

"And now, comrades, I will tell you about my dream of last night. I cannot describe that dream to you. It was a dream of the earth as it will be when Man has vanished. But it reminded me of something that I had long forgotten. Many years ago, when I was a little pig, my mother and the other sows used to sing an old song of which they knew only the tune and the first three words. I had known that tune in my infancy, but it had long since passed out of my mind. Last night, however, it came back to me in my dream. And what is more, the words of the song also came back-words, I am certain, which were sung by the animals of long ago and have been lost to

---

1. Language & Style — It's ironic that while Old Major talks about "perfect unity" between animals, the dogs try to harm the rats. This hints that unity won't be achieved.

2. Theme: Power — All of the animals have a say in decision-making. This makes them a democracy. However, the cat's actions suggest that democracy can be manipulated.

3. Structure — Old Major's warnings foreshadow events later in the story.

4. Key Event — Old Major's speech sows the seeds of rebellion and sets the plot in motion. Without it, the animals may never have considered that a better life was possible.

memory for generations. I will sing you that song now, comrades. I am old and my voice is hoarse, but when I have taught you the tune, you can sing it better for yourselves. It is called 'Beasts of England'."[1]

Old Major cleared his throat and began to sing. As he had said, his voice was hoarse, but he sang well enough, and it was a stirring tune, something between 'Clementine' and 'La Cucaracha'.[2]

The words ran:

> Beasts of England, beasts of Ireland,
> Beasts of every land and clime,
> Hearken to my joyful tidings
> Of the golden future time.
>
> Soon or late the day is coming,
> Tyrant Man shall be o'erthrown,
> And the fruitful fields of England
> Shall be trod by beasts alone.
>
> Rings shall vanish from our noses,
> And the harness from our back,
> Bit and spur shall rust forever,
> Cruel whips no more shall crack.[3]
>
> Riches more than mind can picture,
> Wheat and barley, oats and hay,
> Clover, beans and mangel-wurzels[4]
> Shall be ours upon that day.
>
> Bright will shine the fields of England,
> Purer shall its waters be,
> Sweeter yet shall blow its breezes
> On the day that sets us free.

1. Language & Style — 'Beasts of England' is a satire of the communist anthem 'The Internationale'. At this point in the novella, the song shows the hope that animals will be free from humans.
2. Language & Style — These two tunes are quite humorous and silly, suggesting that 'Beasts of England' (and 'The Internationale') should be seen as absurd.
3. Language & Style — The items listed in this verse are symbols of animal slavery.
4. mangel-wurzels — a type of root vegetable often used to feed animals.

For that day we all must labour,
Though we die before it break;
Cows and horses, geese and turkeys,
All must toil for freedom's sake.

Beasts of England, beasts of Ireland,
Beasts of every land and clime,
Hearken well and spread my tidings
Of the golden future time.

The singing of this song threw the animals into the wildest excitement. Almost before Major had reached the end, they had begun singing it for themselves. Even the stupidest of them had already picked up the tune and a few of the words, and as for the clever ones, such as the pigs and dogs, they had the entire song by heart within a few minutes.[1] And then, after a few preliminary tries, the whole farm burst out into 'Beasts of England' in tremendous unison. The cows lowed it, the dogs whined it, the sheep bleated it, the horses whinnied it, the ducks quacked it. They were so delighted with the song that they sang it right through five times in succession, and might have continued singing it all night if they had not been interrupted.

Unfortunately, the uproar awoke Mr Jones, who sprang out of bed, making sure that there was a fox in the yard. He seized the gun which always stood in a corner of his bedroom, and let fly a charge of Number 6 shot into the darkness. The pellets buried themselves in the wall of the barn and the meeting broke up hurriedly. Everyone fled to his own sleeping-place. The birds jumped on to their perches, the animals settled down in the straw, and the whole farm was asleep in a moment.[2]

---

1. Theme: Power & Language — The pigs' intelligence lets them learn the song faster. This hints at the power their intelligence will bring.

2. Character: Mr Jones — Mr Jones represents Tsar Nicholas II, the powerful and unpopular leader of Russia before the Revolution. Mr Jones's control over the animals here mirrors the Tsar's absolute authority over Russia.

Chapter Two

Three nights later old Major died peacefully in his sleep. His body was buried at the foot of the orchard.

This was early in March. During the next three months there was much secret activity. Major's speech had given to the more intelligent animals on the farm a completely new outlook on life. They did not know when the Rebellion predicted by Major would take place, they had no reason for thinking that it would be within their own lifetime, but they saw clearly that it was their duty to prepare for it. The work of teaching and organising the others fell naturally upon the pigs, who were generally recognised as being the cleverest of the animals.[1] Pre-eminent among the pigs were two young boars named Snowball and Napoleon, whom Mr Jones was breeding up for sale. Napoleon was a large, rather fierce-looking Berkshire boar, the only Berkshire on the farm, not much of a talker, but with a reputation for getting his own way. Snowball was a more vivacious pig than Napoleon, quicker in speech and more inventive, but was not considered to have the same depth of character. All the other male pigs on the farm were porkers[2]. The best known among them was a small fat pig named Squealer, with very round cheeks, twinkling eyes, nimble movements and a shrill voice. He was a brilliant talker, and when he was arguing some difficult point he had a way of skipping from side to side and whisking his tail which was somehow very persuasive. The others said of Squealer that he could turn black into white.[3]

---

1. Theme: Education — The pigs' intelligence is initially a positive thing, as they are able to lead the preparations for the rebellion effectively.
2. porkers — pigs that are fattened up to be killed and eaten.
3. Character: Squealer — Orwell uses antithesis, a technique where opposing words or ideas are presented together to show a contrast. This highlights Squealer's ability to speak persuasively.

These three had elaborated old Major's teachings into a complete system of thought, to which they gave the name of Animalism.[1] Several nights a week, after Mr Jones was asleep, they held secret meetings in the barn and expounded the principles of Animalism to the others. At the beginning they met with much stupidity and apathy. Some of the animals talked of the duty of loyalty to Mr Jones, whom they referred to as "Master," or made elementary remarks such as "Mr Jones feeds us. If he were gone, we should starve to death." Others asked such questions as "Why should we care what happens after we are dead?" or "If this Rebellion is to happen anyway, what difference does it make whether we work for it or not?", and the pigs had great difficulty in making them see that this was contrary to the spirit of Animalism. The stupidest questions of all were asked by Mollie, the white mare. The very first question she asked Snowball was: "Will there still be sugar after the Rebellion?"

"No," said Snowball firmly. "We have no means of making sugar on this farm. Besides, you do not need sugar. You will have all the oats and hay you want."

"And shall I still be allowed to wear ribbons in my mane?" asked Mollie.

"Comrade[2]," said Snowball, "those ribbons that you are so devoted to are the badge of slavery. Can you not understand that liberty is worth more than ribbons?[3]"

Mollie agreed, but she did not sound very convinced.[4]

The pigs had an even harder struggle to counteract the lies put about by Moses, the tame raven. Moses, who was Mr Jones's especial pet, was a spy and a tale-bearer, but he was also a clever talker. He claimed to know of the existence of a mysterious country called

---

1. Background & Context — Throughout the novella, Animalism represents communism, a system of thought which involved equality for all. Russia became a communist country in the early 20th century.

2. Language & Style — Snowball continues Old Major's use of 'comrade', suggesting that he is faithful to the principles of Animalism that Old Major inspired.

3. Key Quote — Animalism is about animal freedom, yet Mollie isn't allowed to wear her ribbons. Denying Mollie this freedom is hypocritical.

4. Character: Mollie — Mollie is more concerned about her luxuries than freedom. She could represent the upper-class Russians who had a comfortable life under the Tsar.

Sugarcandy Mountain, to which all animals went when they died. It was situated somewhere up in the sky, a little distance beyond the clouds, Moses said. In Sugarcandy Mountain it was Sunday seven days a week, clover was in season all the year round, and lump sugar and linseed cake grew on the hedges. The animals hated Moses because he told tales and did no work, but some of them believed in Sugarcandy Mountain, and the pigs had to argue very hard to persuade them that there was no such place.[1]

Their most faithful disciples were the two cart-horses, Boxer and Clover. These two had great difficulty in thinking anything out for themselves, but having once accepted the pigs as their teachers, they absorbed everything that they were told, and passed it on to the other animals by simple arguments.[2] They were unfailing in their attendance at the secret meetings in the barn, and led the singing of 'Beasts of England', with which the meetings always ended.

Now, as it turned out, the Rebellion was achieved much earlier and more easily than anyone had expected. In past years Mr Jones, although a hard master, had been a capable farmer, but of late he had fallen on evil days. He had become much disheartened after losing money in a lawsuit, and had taken to drinking more than was good for him. For whole days at a time he would lounge in his windsor chair in the kitchen, reading the newspapers, drinking, and occasionally feeding Moses on crusts of bread soaked in beer. His men were idle and dishonest, the fields were full of weeds, the buildings wanted roofing, the hedges were neglected and the animals were underfed.[3]

June came and the hay was almost ready for cutting. On Midsummer's Eve, which was a Saturday, Mr Jones went into Willingdon and got so drunk at the Red Lion that he did not come back till midday on Sunday. The men had milked the cows in the

1. Character: Moses — Moses represents religion. He reflects Karl Marx's belief that religion stopped people doing something about the poor conditions in their current life, because they believed there was a happier afterlife still to come.
2. Theme: Education — The other animals (in this case, Boxer and Clover) spread the pigs' teaching without question. This becomes problematic later in the story.
3. Character: Mr Jones — Mr Jones's total power on the farm has made him complacent. He doesn't realise that there might be consequences to treating the animals poorly.

early morning and then had gone out rabbiting, without bothering to feed the animals. When Mr Jones got back he immediately went to sleep on the drawing-room sofa with the News of the World over his face, so that when evening came the animals were still unfed. At last they could stand it no longer. One of the cows broke in the door of the store-shed with her horn and all the animals began to help themselves from the bins. It was just then that Mr Jones woke up. The next moment he and his four men were in the store-shed with whips in their hands, lashing out in all directions. This was more than the hungry animals could bear. With one accord, though nothing of the kind had been planned beforehand, they flung themselves upon their tormentors.[1] Jones and his men suddenly found themselves being butted and kicked from all sides. The situation was quite out of their control. They had never seen animals behave like this before, and this sudden uprising of creatures whom they were used to thrashing and maltreating just as they chose, frightened them almost out of their wits. After only a moment or two they gave up trying to defend themselves and took to their heels. A minute later all five of them were in full flight down the cart-track that led to the main road, with the animals pursuing them in triumph.[2]

Mrs Jones looked out of the bedroom window, saw what was happening, hurriedly flung a few possessions into a carpet bag and slipped out of the farm by another way. Moses sprang off his perch and flapped after her, croaking loudly. Meanwhile the animals had chased Jones and his men out on to the road and slammed the five-barred gate behind them. And so, almost before they knew what was happening, the Rebellion had been successfully carried through; Jones was expelled, and the Manor Farm was theirs.[3]

For the first few minutes the animals could hardly believe in their good fortune. Their first act was to gallop in a body right round the boundaries of the farm, as though to make quite sure that no human

---

1. Language & Style — The whips are symbols of slavery, which the animals fight against.
2. Background & Context — This rebellion has similarities to the February Revolution in 1917, when the Russian Tsar was overthrown. The February Revolution started spontaneously during a demonstration about food shortages.
3. Key Event — The animals remove Jones from the farm and secure their freedom.

being was hiding anywhere upon it; then they raced back to the farm buildings to wipe out the last traces of Jones's hated reign. The harness-room at the end of the stables was broken open; the bits, the nose-rings, the dog-chains, the cruel knives with which Mr Jones had been used to castrate the pigs and lambs, were all flung down the well. The reins, the halters, the blinkers, the degrading nosebags, were thrown onto the rubbish fire which was burning in the yard. So were the whips. All the animals capered with joy when they saw the whips going up in flames. Snowball also threw on to the fire the ribbons with which the horses' manes and tails had usually been decorated on market days.[1]

"Ribbons," he said, "should be considered as clothes, which are the mark of a human being. All animals should go naked."

When Boxer heard this he fetched the small straw hat which he wore in summer to keep the flies out of his ears, and flung it onto the fire with the rest.[2]

In a very little while the animals had destroyed everything that reminded them of Mr Jones. Napoleon then led them back to the store-shed and served out a double ration of corn to everybody, with two biscuits for each dog. Then they sang 'Beasts of England' from end to end seven times running, and after that they settled down for the night and slept as they had never slept before.

But they woke at dawn as usual, and suddenly remembering the glorious thing that had happened, they all raced out into the pasture together. A little way down the pasture there was a knoll that commanded a view of most of the farm. The animals rushed to the top of it and gazed round them in the clear morning light.[3] Yes, it was theirs — everything that they could see was theirs! In the ecstasy of that thought they gambolled round and round, they hurled themselves into the air in great leaps of excitement. They rolled in the dew, they cropped mouthfuls of the sweet summer grass, they

---

1. Character: Snowball — By removing the ribbons, Snowball prioritises following Animalism strictly, even though it will upset Mollie.
2. Theme: Animalism — Boxer throws away the hat, despite it helping him. This hints that blindly following the principles of Animalism could cause the animals to suffer.
3. Language & Style — The dawn symbolises the new hope that the rebellion brings.

kicked up clods of the black earth and snuffed its rich scent. Then they made a tour of inspection of the whole farm and surveyed with speechless admiration the ploughland, the hayfield, the orchard, the pool, the spinney[1].[2] It was as though they had never seen these things before, and even now they could hardly believe that it was all their own.

Then they filed back to the farm buildings and halted in silence outside the door of the farmhouse. That was theirs too, but they were frightened to go inside. After a moment, however, Snowball and Napoleon butted the door open with their shoulders and the animals entered in single file, walking with the utmost care for fear of disturbing anything.[3] They tiptoed from room to room, afraid to speak above a whisper and gazing with a kind of awe at the unbelievable luxury, at the beds with their feather mattresses, the looking-glasses, the horsehair sofa, the Brussels carpet, the lithograph of Queen Victoria over the drawing-room mantelpiece. They were just coming down the stairs when Mollie was discovered to be missing. Going back, the others found that she had remained behind in the best bedroom. She had taken a piece of blue ribbon from Mrs Jones's dressing-table, and was holding it against her shoulder and admiring herself in the glass in a very foolish manner. The others reproached her sharply, and they went outside. Some hams hanging in the kitchen were taken out for burial, and the barrel of beer in the scullery was stove in with a kick from Boxer's hoof, otherwise nothing in the house was touched. A unanimous resolution was passed on the spot that the farmhouse should be preserved as a museum. All were agreed that no animal must ever live there.

The animals had their breakfast, and then Snowball and Napoleon called them together again.

"Comrades," said Snowball, "it is half-past six and we have a long

---

1. spinney — a small area with trees.
2. Language & Style — The list highlights how much the animals have gained, but also how much they were deprived of under Jones's rule.
3. Characters: Snowball & Napoleon — The two pigs lead the animals into the farmhouse together. This shows that, at this moment, Snowball and Napoleon are equals.

day before us. Today we begin the hay harvest. But there is another matter that must be attended to first."

The pigs now revealed that during the past three months they had taught themselves to read and write from an old spelling book which had belonged to Mr Jones's children and which had been thrown on the rubbish heap.[1] Napoleon sent for pots of black and white paint and led the way down to the five-barred gate that gave on to the main road. Then Snowball (for it was Snowball who was best at writing) took a brush between the two knuckles of his trotter, painted out MANOR FARM from the top bar of the gate and in its place painted ANIMAL FARM. This was to be the name of the farm from now onwards. After this they went back to the farm buildings, where Snowball and Napoleon sent for a ladder which they caused to be set against the end wall of the big barn. They explained that by their studies of the past three months the pigs had succeeded in reducing the principles of Animalism to seven commandments. These seven commandments would now be inscribed on the wall; they would form an unalterable law by which all the animals on Animal Farm must live for ever after. With some difficulty (for it is not easy for a pig to balance himself on a ladder) Snowball climbed up and set to work, with Squealer a few rungs below him holding the paint-pot. The commandments were written on the tarred wall in great white letters that could be read thirty yards away. They ran thus:

THE SEVEN COMMANDMENTS[2]
1. Whatever goes upon two legs is an enemy.
2. Whatever goes upon four legs, or has wings, is a friend.
3. No animal shall wear clothes.
4. No animal shall sleep in a bed.
5. No animal shall drink alcohol.
6. No animal shall kill any other animal.
7. All animals are equal.

---

1. Theme: Education & Social Class — The pigs teaching themselves to read gives them an advantage over the other animals, increasing their power and status.
2. Key Event — The principles of Animalism have been turned into rules by the pigs. The pigs are now acting as an authority and are in charge of the other animals.

It was very neatly written, and except that "friend" was written "freind" and one of the "S's" was the wrong way round, the spelling was correct all the way through. Snowball read it aloud for the benefit of the others. All the animals nodded in complete agreement, and the cleverer ones at once began to learn the commandments by heart.

"Now, comrades," cried Snowball, throwing down the paintbrush, "to the hayfield! Let us make it a point of honour to get in the harvest more quickly than Jones and his men could do."

But at this moment the three cows, who had seemed uneasy for some time past, set up a loud lowing. They had not been milked for twenty-four hours, and their udders were almost bursting. After a little thought, the pigs sent for buckets and milked the cows fairly successfully, their trotters being well adapted to this task. Soon there were five buckets of frothing creamy milk at which many of the animals looked with considerable interest.

"What is going to happen to all that milk?" said someone.

"Jones used sometimes to mix some of it in our mash," said one of the hens.

"Never mind the milk, comrades!" cried Napoleon, placing himself in front of the buckets. "That will be attended to. The harvest is more important. Comrade Snowball will lead the way. I shall follow in a few minutes. Forward, comrades! The hay is waiting."[1]

So the animals trooped down to the hayfield to begin the harvest, and when they came back in the evening it was noticed that the milk had disappeared.[2][3]

---

1. Character: Napoleon — This is the first time in the novella that Napoleon speaks. He aims to distract the animals and steal the milk. It's the reader's first insight into Napoleon's selfishness and cunning.

2. Narrative Viewpoint — The narrative viewpoint is limited as it only presents what the animals see and hear. The reader is forced to draw their own conclusions.

3. Structure — This ending to the chapter hints that there are already divisions amongst the animals, and suggests that there are more problems to come, creating tension.

Chapter Three

How they toiled and sweated to get the hay in! But their efforts were rewarded, for the harvest was an even bigger success than they had hoped.

Sometimes the work was hard; the implements had been designed for human beings and not for animals, and it was a great drawback that no animal was able to use any tool that involved standing on his hind legs. But the pigs were so clever that they could think of a way round every difficulty. As for the horses, they knew every inch of the field, and in fact understood the business of mowing and raking far better than Jones and his men had ever done. The pigs did not actually work, but directed and supervised the others.[1] With their superior knowledge it was natural that they should assume the leadership. Boxer and Clover would harness themselves to the cutter or the horse-rake (no bits or reins were needed in these days, of course) and tramp steadily round and round the field with a pig walking behind and calling out "Gee up, comrade!" or "Whoa back, comrade!" as the case might be. And every animal down to the humblest worked at turning the hay and gathering it. Even the ducks and hens toiled to and fro all day in the sun, carrying tiny wisps of hay in their beaks. In the end they finished the harvest in two days' less time than it had usually taken Jones and his men. Moreover, it was the biggest harvest that the farm had ever seen.[2] There was no wastage whatever; the hens and ducks with their sharp eyes had gathered up the very last stalk. And not an animal on the

---

1. Characters: The Pigs — The pigs begin to treat themselves differently to the other animals. They leave the hard work to the others and give themselves tasks with no physical labour.
2. Theme: Animalism — Being in charge of the farm motivates the animals to work harder and achieve better results.

farm had stolen so much as a mouthful.[1]

All through that summer the work of the farm went like clockwork. The animals were happy as they had never conceived it possible to be. Every mouthful of food was an acute positive pleasure, now that it was truly their own food, produced by themselves and for themselves, not doled out to them by a grudging master. With the worthless parasitical human beings gone, there was more for everyone to eat. There was more leisure too, inexperienced though the animals were. They met with many difficulties — for instance, later in the year, when they harvested the corn, they had to tread it out in the ancient style and blow away the chaff with their breath, since the farm possessed no threshing machine — but the pigs with their cleverness and Boxer with his tremendous muscles always pulled them through.[2] Boxer was the admiration of everybody.[3] He had been a hard worker even in Jones's time, but now he seemed more like three horses than one; there were days when the entire work of the farm seemed to rest upon his mighty shoulders. From morning to night he was pushing and pulling, always at the spot where the work was hardest. He had made an arrangement with one of the cockerels to call him in the mornings half an hour earlier than anyone else, and would put in some volunteer labour at whatever seemed to be most needed, before the regular day's work began. His answer to every problem, every setback, was "I will work harder!" — which he had adopted as his personal motto.

But everyone worked according to his capacity. The hens and ducks, for instance, saved five bushels of corn at the harvest by gathering up the stray grains. Nobody stole, nobody grumbled over his rations, the quarrelling and biting and jealousy which had been normal features of life in the old days had almost disappeared. Nobody shirked — or almost nobody. Mollie, it was true, was not good at getting up in the mornings, and had a way of leaving work early on the ground that there was a stone in her hoof. And the behaviour of the cat was somewhat peculiar. It was soon noticed that when

---

1. Language & Style — This comment is ironic, as the pigs have stolen the milk.
2. Theme: Animalism — The animals use their strengths to benefit each other.
3. Character: Boxer — Boxer's hardworking nature makes him popular with the others.

there was work to be done the cat could never be found. She would vanish for hours on end, and then reappear at meal-times, or in the evening after work was over, as though nothing had happened.[1] But she always made such excellent excuses, and purred so affectionately, that it was impossible not to believe in her good intentions. Old Benjamin, the donkey, seemed quite unchanged since the Rebellion. He did his work in the same slow obstinate way as he had done it in Jones's time, never shirking and never volunteering for extra work either. About the Rebellion and its results he would express no opinion. When asked whether he was not happier now that Jones was gone, he would say only "Donkeys live a long time. None of you has ever seen a dead donkey," and the others had to be content with this cryptic answer.[2]

On Sundays there was no work. Breakfast was an hour later than usual, and after breakfast there was a ceremony which was observed every week without fail. First came the hoisting of the flag. Snowball had found in the harness-room an old green tablecloth of Mrs Jones's and had painted on it a hoof and a horn in white. This was run up the flagstaff in the farmhouse garden every Sunday morning. The flag was green, Snowball explained, to represent the green fields of England, while the hoof and horn signified the future Republic of the Animals which would arise when the human race had been finally overthrown.[3] After the hoisting of the flag all the animals trooped into the big barn for a general assembly which was known as the Meeting. Here the work of the coming week was planned out and resolutions were put forward and debated. It was always the pigs who put forward the resolutions. The other animals understood how to vote, but could never think of any resolutions of their own.[4]

---

1. Theme: Animalism — Not all the animals work hard. This hints at the difficulty of leading a revolution and getting everyone to work towards a common goal.
2. Character: Benjamin — Benjamin's cynicism brings a dark tone to the pleasant atmosphere. It hints that there are tricky times ahead for the animals.
3. Language & Style — The flag is a symbol of animal freedom. It is similar to the real-life flag of the Soviet Union, which had a hammer and sickle to represent the workers and peasants.
4. Theme: Power — Although there is still a democracy, the pigs ultimately control what happens on the farm due to their intelligence.

20

Snowball and Napoleon were by far the most active in the debates. But it was noticed that these two were never in agreement: whatever suggestion either of them made, the other could be counted on to oppose it. Even when it was resolved — a thing no one could object to in itself — to set aside the small paddock behind the orchard as a home of rest for animals who were past work, there was a stormy debate over the correct retiring age for each class of animal. The Meeting always ended with the singing of 'Beasts of England', and the afternoon was given up to recreation.

The pigs had set aside the harness-room as a headquarters for themselves.[1] Here, in the evenings, they studied blacksmithing, carpentering and other necessary arts from books which they had brought out of the farmhouse. Snowball also busied himself with organising the other animals into what he called Animal Committees. He was indefatigable at this. He formed the Egg Production Committee for the hens, the Clean Tails League for the cows, the Wild Comrades' Re-education Committee (the object of this was to tame the rats and rabbits), the Whiter Wool Movement for the sheep, and various others, besides instituting classes in reading and writing. On the whole, these projects were a failure.[2] The attempt to tame the wild creatures, for instance, broke down almost immediately. They continued to behave very much as before, and when treated with generosity, simply took advantage of it. The cat joined the Re-education Committee and was very active in it for some days. She was seen one day sitting on a roof and talking to some sparrows who were just out of her reach. She was telling them that all animals were now comrades and that any sparrow who chose could come and perch on her paw; but the sparrows kept their distance.

The reading and writing classes, however, were a great success. By the autumn almost every animal on the farm was literate in some degree.

As for the pigs, they could already read and write perfectly. The

---

1. Characters: The Pigs — By separating themselves, the pigs behave like they're superior.
2. Character: Snowball — The failure of Snowball's committees suggests that he is idealistic about what the animals are capable of achieving.

dogs learned to read fairly well, but were not interested in reading anything except the Seven Commandments. Muriel, the goat, could read somewhat better than the dogs, and sometimes used to read to the others in the evenings from scraps of newspaper which she found on the rubbish heap. Benjamin could read as well as any pig, but never exercised his faculty. So far as he knew, he said, there was nothing worth reading.[1] Clover learnt the whole alphabet, but could not put words together. Boxer could not get beyond the letter D. He would trace out A, B, C, D in the dust with his great hoof, and then would stand staring at the letters with his ears back, sometimes shaking his forelock, trying with all his might to remember what came next and never succeeding. On several occasions, indeed, he did learn E, F, G, H, but by the time he knew them it was always discovered that he had forgotten A, B, C and D. Finally he decided to be content with the first four letters, and used to write them out once or twice every day to refresh his memory. Mollie refused to learn any but the five letters which spelt her own name.[2] She would form these very neatly out of pieces of twig, and would then decorate them with a flower or two and walk round them admiring them.

None of the other animals on the farm could get further than the letter A. It was also found that the stupider animals, such as the sheep, hens, and ducks, were unable to learn the Seven Commandments by heart. After much thought Snowball declared that the Seven Commandments could in effect be reduced to a single maxim, namely: "Four legs good, two legs bad."[3] This, he said, contained the essential principle of Animalism. Whoever had thoroughly grasped it would be safe from human influences. The birds at first objected, since it seemed to them that they also had two legs, but Snowball proved to them that this was not so.

"A bird's wing, comrades," he said, "is an organ of propulsion

---

1. Character: Benjamin — Benjamin is as smart as the pigs, but he has no desire to challenge them. He represents intellectual Russians (the 'intelligentsia'), who saw that communism wouldn't solve society's problems, but did nothing to stop Stalin.

2. Character: Mollie — Mollie is intelligent enough to learn the alphabet, but she's limited by her own selfishness and only learns the letters that she sees as relevant to her.

3. Key Quote — This statement aims to simplify Animalism for the less intelligent animals. However, its purpose and meaning is manipulated later in the story.

and not of manipulation. It should therefore be regarded as a leg. The distinguishing mark of man is the *hand*, the instrument with which he does all his mischief."

The birds did not understand Snowball's long words, but they accepted his explanation, and all the humbler animals set to work to learn the new maxim by heart. FOUR LEGS GOOD, TWO LEGS BAD, was inscribed on the end wall of the barn, above the Seven Commandments and in bigger letters. When they had once got it by heart, the sheep developed a great liking for this maxim, and often as they lay in the field they would all start bleating "Four legs good, two legs bad! Four legs good, two legs bad!" and keep it up for hours on end, never growing tired of it.

Napoleon took no interest in Snowball's committees. He said that the education of the young was more important than anything that could be done for those who were already grown up. It happened that Jessie and Bluebell had both whelped soon after the hay harvest, giving birth between them to nine sturdy puppies. As soon as they were weaned, Napoleon took them away from their mothers,[1] saying that he would make himself responsible for their education. He took them up into a loft which could only be reached by a ladder from the harness-room, and there kept them in such seclusion that the rest of the farm soon forgot their existence.[2]

The mystery of where the milk went to was soon cleared up. It was mixed every day into the pigs' mash. The early apples were now ripening, and the grass of the orchard was littered with windfalls.[3] The animals had assumed as a matter of course that these would be shared out equally; one day, however, the order went forth that all the windfalls were to be collected and brought to the harness-room for the use of the pigs. At this some of the other animals murmured, but it was no use. All the pigs were in full agreement on this point, even

---

1. Structure — In Chapter One, Old Major highlighted man's cruelty in taking animals from their mothers. Napoleon's actions here mirror this, which suggests that he may be similarly cruel.

2. Theme: Power — Napoleon recognises that the young are easier to influence, and that having them on his side will provide him with greater power in the future.

3. windfalls — fruit (in this case apples) that has fallen from a tree.

Snowball and Napoleon. Squealer was sent to make the necessary explanations to the others.

"Comrades!" he cried. "You do not imagine, I hope, that we pigs are doing this in a spirit of selfishness and privilege? Many of us actually dislike milk and apples. I dislike them myself. Our sole object in taking these things is to preserve our health. Milk and apples (this has been proved by Science, comrades) contain substances absolutely necessary to the well-being of a pig. We pigs are brainworkers. The whole management and organisation of this farm depend on us. Day and night we are watching over your welfare. It is for *your* sake that we drink that milk and eat those apples.[1] Do you know what would happen if we pigs failed in our duty? Jones would come back! Yes, Jones would come back! Surely, comrades," cried Squealer almost pleadingly, skipping from side to side and whisking his tail, "surely there is no one among you who wants to see Jones come back?"[2]

Now if there was one thing that the animals were completely certain of, it was that they did not want Jones back. When it was put to them in this light, they had no more to say. The importance of keeping the pigs in good health was all too obvious. So it was agreed without further argument that the milk and the windfall apples (and also the main crop of apples when they ripened) should be reserved for the pigs alone.[3]

---

1. Theme: Propaganda — Propaganda is when a group spreads information (often exaggerated or made up) to make themselves look good. It is used here to persuade the animals that the pigs are taking the milk and apples for the benefit of the farm.

2. Character: Squealer — Squealer uses the fear of Mr Jones to influence the animals. He is manipulative and willing to scare the animals to keep them in line.

3. Key Event — The milk and apples incident is the clearest incident yet of the pigs abusing their power. It's also the first time they use Squealer's propaganda to influence the animals. The reader can see that the pigs aren't acting in the animals' best interest.

Chapter Four

By the late summer the news of what had happened on Animal Farm had spread across half the county. Every day Snowball and Napoleon sent out flights of pigeons whose instructions were to mingle with the animals on neighbouring farms, tell them the story of the Rebellion, and teach them the tune of 'Beasts of England'.

Most of this time Mr Jones had spent sitting in the taproom of the Red Lion at Willingdon, complaining to anyone who would listen of the monstrous injustice he had suffered in being turned out of his property by a pack of good-for-nothing animals. The other farmers sympathised in principle, but they did not at first give him much help. At heart, each of them was secretly wondering whether he could not somehow turn Jones's misfortune to his own advantage.[1] It was lucky that the owners of the two farms which adjoined Animal Farm were on permanently bad terms. One of them, which was named Foxwood, was a large, neglected, old-fashioned farm, much overgrown by woodland, with all its pastures worn out and its hedges in a disgraceful condition. Its owner, Mr Pilkington, was an easy-going gentleman-farmer who spent most of his time in fishing or hunting according to the season. The other farm, which was called Pinchfield, was smaller and better kept. Its owner was a Mr Frederick, a tough, shrewd man, perpetually involved in lawsuits and with a name for driving hard bargains. These two disliked each other so much that it was difficult for them to come to any agreement, even in defence of their own interests.[2]

---

1. Characters: The Humans — The humans are untrustworthy and don't support their fellow human, Mr Jones. Instead, they try to profit from his misfortune.
2. Characters: Mr Pilkington & Mr Frederick — Mr Pilkington can be seen to represent Britain and the USA, while Frederick represents Hitler and Nazi Germany. The bad relations between these farmers reflects the political tension between these nations.

Nevertheless, they were both thoroughly frightened by the rebellion on Animal Farm, and very anxious to prevent their own animals from learning too much about it. At first they pretended to laugh to scorn the idea of animals managing a farm for themselves. The whole thing would be over in a fortnight, they said. They put it about that the animals on the Manor Farm (they insisted on calling it the Manor Farm; they would not tolerate the name "Animal Farm") were perpetually fighting among themselves and were also rapidly starving to death. When time passed and the animals had evidently not starved to death, Frederick and Pilkington changed their tune and began to talk of the terrible wickedness that now flourished on Animal Farm. It was given out that the animals there practised cannibalism, tortured one another with red-hot horseshoes and had their females in common. This was what came of rebelling against the laws of Nature, Frederick and Pilkington said.[1]

However, these stories were never fully believed. Rumours of a wonderful farm, where the human beings had been turned out and the animals managed their own affairs, continued to circulate in vague and distorted forms, and throughout that year a wave of rebelliousness ran through the countryside. Bulls which had always been tractable suddenly turned savage, sheep broke down hedges and devoured the clover, cows kicked the pail over, hunters refused their fences and shot their riders on to the other side. Above all, the tune and even the words of 'Beasts of England' were known everywhere. It had spread with astonishing speed. The human beings could not contain their rage when they heard this song, though they pretended to think it merely ridiculous. They could not understand, they said, how even animals could bring themselves to sing such contemptible rubbish. Any animal caught singing it was given a flogging on the spot. And yet the song was irrepressible. The blackbirds whistled it in the hedges, the pigeons cooed it in the elms, it got into the din of the smithies and the tune of the church bells. And when the human beings listened to it, they secretly trembled, hearing in it a prophecy

---

1. Theme: Propaganda — Frederick and Pilkington spread rumours to discourage their own animals from rebelling. This reflects the fears of world leaders who worried their people might rebel like the Russians.

of their future doom.

Early in October, when the corn was cut and stacked and some of it was already threshed, a flight of pigeons came whirling through the air and alighted in the yard of Animal Farm in the wildest excitement. Jones and all his men, with half a dozen others from Foxwood and Pinchfield, had entered the five-barred gate and were coming up the cart-track that led to the farm. They were all carrying sticks, except Jones, who was marching ahead with a gun in his hands. Obviously they were going to attempt the recapture of the farm.

This had long been expected, and all preparations had been made. Snowball, who had studied an old book of Julius Caesar's[1] campaigns which he had found in the farmhouse, was in charge of the defensive operations. He gave his orders quickly, and in a couple of minutes every animal was at his post.[2]

As the human beings approached the farm buildings, Snowball launched his first attack. All the pigeons, to the number of thirty-five, flew to and fro over the men's heads and dropped their dung on them from mid-air; and while the men were dealing with this, the geese, who had been hiding behind the hedge, rushed out and pecked viciously at the calves of their legs. However, this was only a light skirmishing manoeuvre, intended to create a little disorder, and the men easily drove the geese off with their sticks. Snowball now launched his second line of attack. Muriel, Benjamin, and all the sheep, with Snowball at the head of them, rushed forward and prodded and butted the men from every side, while Benjamin turned round and lashed at them with his small hoofs. But once again the men, with their sticks and their hobnailed boots, were too strong for them; and suddenly, at a squeal from Snowball, which was the signal for retreat, all the animals turned and fled through the gateway into the yard.

---

1. Background & Context — Caesar was a powerful Roman leader, but he was betrayed by his allies. Mentioning him here hints that Snowball may suffer a similar fate.
2. Character: Snowball — Snowball represents Trotsky, a skilled leader in the Communist party who was able to organise a powerful army. Like Trotsky, Snowball shows skill and strategy in commanding the animals.

The men gave a shout of triumph. They saw, as they imagined, their enemies in flight, and they rushed after them in disorder. This was just what Snowball had intended. As soon as they were well inside the yard, the three horses, the three cows and the rest of the pigs, who had been lying in ambush in the cowshed, suddenly emerged in their rear, cutting them off. Snowball now gave the signal for the charge. He himself dashed straight for Jones. Jones saw him coming, raised his gun and fired. The pellets scored bloody streaks along Snowball's back, and a sheep dropped dead.[1] Without halting for an instant, Snowball flung his fifteen stone against Jones's legs.[2] Jones was hurled into a pile of dung and his gun flew out of his hands. But the most terrifying spectacle of all was Boxer, rearing up on his hind legs and striking out with his great iron-shod hoofs like a stallion. His very first blow took a stable-lad from Foxwood on the skull and stretched him lifeless in the mud. At the sight, several men dropped their sticks and tried to run. Panic overtook them, and the next moment all the animals together were chasing them round and round the yard. They were gored, kicked, bitten, trampled on. There was not an animal on the farm that did not take vengeance on them after his own fashion. Even the cat suddenly leapt off a roof onto a cowman's shoulders and sank her claws in his neck, at which he yelled horribly. At a moment when the opening was clear, the men were glad enough to rush out of the yard and make a bolt for the main road. And so within five minutes of their invasion they were in ignominious retreat by the same way as they had come, with a flock of geese hissing after them and pecking at their calves all the way.[3]

All the men were gone except one. Back in the yard Boxer was pawing with his hoof at the stable-lad who lay face down in the mud, trying to turn him over. The boy did not stir.

"He is dead," said Boxer sorrowfully. "I had no intention of

1. Language & Style — Orwell uses very simple, unemotional language to describe the sheep's death. It makes her death seem irrelevant in the bigger picture of the battle.
2. Characters: Snowball & Napoleon — Snowball is fearless in battle. In contrast, Napoleon isn't mentioned, which suggests he doesn't play a significant role in the fight.
3. Background & Context — This battle represents the civil war in Russia between the Bolsheviks and those who were loyal to the Tsar. The Bolshevik army, led by Trotsky, won the war.

doing that. I forgot that I was wearing iron shoes. Who will believe that I did not do this on purpose?"

"No sentimentality, comrade!" cried Snowball, from whose wounds the blood was still dripping. "War is war. The only good human being is a dead one.[1]"

"I have no wish to take life, not even human life," repeated Boxer, and his eyes were full of tears.[2]

"Where is Mollie?" exclaimed somebody.

Mollie in fact was missing. For a moment there was great alarm; it was feared that the men might have harmed her in some way, or even carried her off with them. In the end, however, she was found hiding in her stall with her head buried among the hay in the manger. She had taken to flight as soon as the gun went off. And when the others came back from looking for her, it was to find that the stable-lad, who in fact was only stunned, had already recovered and made off.

The animals had now reassembled in the wildest excitement, each recounting his own exploits in the battle at the top of his voice. An impromptu celebration of the victory was held immediately. The flag was run up and 'Beasts of England' was sung a number of times, then the sheep who had been killed was given a solemn funeral, a hawthorn bush being planted on her grave. At the graveside Snowball made a little speech, emphasising the need for all animals to be ready to die for Animal Farm if need be.

The animals decided unanimously to create a military decoration, 'Animal Hero, First Class', which was conferred there and then on Snowball and Boxer. It consisted of a brass medal (they were really some old horse-brasses which had been found in the harness-room), to be worn on Sundays and holidays. There was also 'Animal Hero, Second Class', which was conferred posthumously on the dead sheep.[3]

---

1. Key Quote — Snowball's desire for animal freedom makes him cold-hearted and violent.
2. Character: Boxer — Boxer's regret about his actions is juxtaposed with Snowball's ruthless attitude. Their contrasting reactions emphasise Boxer's gentle nature.
3. Theme: Social Class — The medals establish an inequality amongst the animals. Snowball and Boxer are now seen to be a higher class of animal.

There was much discussion as to what the battle should be called. In the end, it was named the Battle of the Cowshed, since that was where the ambush had been sprung. Mr Jones's gun had been found lying in the mud, and it was known that there was a supply of cartridges in the farmhouse. It was decided to set the gun up at the foot of the flagstaff, like a piece of artillery, and to fire it twice a year — once on October the twelfth, the anniversary of the Battle of the Cowshed, and once on Midsummer Day, the anniversary of the Rebellion.[12]

---

1. Theme: Power — The gun, which symbolises power and control, is now in the possession of the animals rather than the humans.
2. Key Event — The Battle of the Cowshed shows that the animals can overcome the humans when they work together. It shows Animalism at its most successful.

Chapter Five

As winter drew on, Mollie became more and more troublesome.[1] She was late for work every morning and excused herself by saying that she had overslept, and she complained of mysterious pains, although her appetite was excellent. On every kind of pretext she would run away from work and go to the drinking pool, where she would stand foolishly gazing at her own reflection in the water. But there were also rumours of something more serious. One day, as Mollie strolled blithely into the yard, flirting her long tail and chewing at a stalk of hay, Clover took her aside.

"Mollie," she said, "I have something very serious to say to you. This morning I saw you looking over the hedge that divides Animal Farm from Foxwood. One of Mr Pilkington's men was standing on the other side of the hedge. And — I was a long way away, but I am almost certain I saw this — he was talking to you and you were allowing him to stroke your nose. What does that mean, Mollie?"

"He didn't! I wasn't! It isn't true!" cried Mollie, beginning to prance about and paw the ground.

"Mollie! Look me in the face. Do you give me your word of honour that that man was not stroking your nose?"[2]

"It isn't true!" repeated Mollie, but she could not look Clover in the face, and the next moment she took to her heels and galloped away into the field.

A thought struck Clover. Without saying anything to the others, she went to Mollie's stall and turned over the straw with her hoof. Hidden under the straw was a little pile of lump sugar and several

---

1. Structure — This is the first chapter set in winter, which creates a shift in tone from the celebratory mood of the previous chapter.
2. Character: Clover — Clover confronts Mollie, suggesting she's loyal to Animalism, but she also seems concerned for Mollie, which shows her maternal, caring side.

bunches of ribbon of different colours.

Three days later Mollie disappeared. For some weeks nothing was known of her whereabouts, then the pigeons reported that they had seen her on the other side of Willingdon. She was between the shafts of a smart dogcart[1] painted red and black, which was standing outside a public-house. A fat red-faced man in check breeches and gaiters, who looked like a publican, was stroking her nose and feeding her with sugar.[2] Her coat was newly clipped and she wore a scarlet ribbon round her forelock. She appeared to be enjoying herself, so the pigeons said. None of the animals ever mentioned Mollie again.

In January there came bitterly hard weather. The earth was like iron, and nothing could be done in the fields. Many meetings were held in the big barn, and the pigs occupied themselves with planning out the work of the coming season. It had come to be accepted that the pigs, who were manifestly cleverer than the other animals, should decide all questions of farm policy, though their decisions had to be ratified by a majority vote. This arrangement would have worked well enough if it had not been for the disputes between Snowball and Napoleon. These two disagreed at every point where disagreement was possible. If one of them suggested sowing a bigger acreage with barley, the other was certain to demand a bigger acreage of oats, and if one of them said that such and such a field was just right for cabbages, the other would declare that it was useless for anything except roots. Each had his own following, and there were some violent debates. At the Meetings Snowball often won over the majority by his brilliant speeches, but Napoleon was better at canvassing support for himself in between times.[3] He was especially successful with the sheep. Of late the sheep had taken to bleating "Four legs good, two legs bad" both in and out of season, and they often interrupted the Meeting with this. It was noticed that they were especially liable to break into "Four legs good, two legs bad" at

---

1. dogcart — a two-wheeled horse-drawn vehicle.
2. Character: Mollie — Mollie's desire for luxuries leads to her giving up her freedom.
3. Background & Context — Stalin gained power over Trotsky because he surrounded himself with loyal followers, just as Napoleon does here.

crucial moments in Snowball's speeches.[1] Snowball had made a close study of some back numbers of the 'Farmer and Stockbreeder' which he had found in the farmhouse, and was full of plans for innovations and improvements. He talked learnedly about field-drains, silage[2] and basic slag[3], and had worked out a complicated scheme for all the animals to drop their dung directly in the fields, at a different spot every day, to save the labour of cartage. Napoleon produced no schemes of his own, but said quietly that Snowball's would come to nothing, and seemed to be biding his time. But of all their controversies, none was so bitter as the one that took place over the windmill.

In the long pasture, not far from the farm buildings, there was a small knoll which was the highest point on the farm. After surveying the ground, Snowball declared that this was just the place for a windmill, which could be made to operate a dynamo and supply the farm with electrical power. This would light the stalls and warm them in winter, and would also run a circular saw, a chaff-cutter, a mangel-slicer[4] and an electric milking machine. The animals had never heard of anything of this kind before (for the farm was an old-fashioned one and had only the most primitive machinery), and they listened in astonishment while Snowball conjured up pictures of fantastic machines which would do their work for them while they grazed at their ease in the fields or improved their minds with reading and conversation.[5]

Within a few weeks Snowball's plans for the windmill were fully worked out. The mechanical details came mostly from three books which had belonged to Mr Jones — 'One Thousand Useful Things to Do About the House', 'Every Man His Own Bricklayer', and 'Electricity for Beginners'. Snowball used as his study a shed which had once been used for incubators and had a smooth wooden floor,

---

1. Language & Style — It's ironic that this phrase, which Snowball invented to help the sheep, is now being used against him.
2. silage — food that is used to feed cattle in dry seasons.
3. basic slag — waste products that can be used as animal fertiliser.
4. mangel-slicer — a machine that cuts up mangel-wurzels (a type of root vegetable).
5. Language & Style — The windmill represents the idealised future the animals dream of.

suitable for drawing on. He was closeted there for hours at a time. With his books held open by a stone, and with a piece of chalk gripped between the knuckles of his trotter, he would move rapidly to and fro, drawing in line after line and uttering little whimpers of excitement. Gradually the plans grew into a complicated mass of cranks and cog-wheels, covering more than half the floor, which the other animals found completely unintelligible but very impressive. All of them came to look at Snowball's drawings at least once a day. Even the hens and ducks came, and were at pains not to tread on the chalk marks. Only Napoleon held aloof. He had declared himself against the windmill from the start. One day, however, he arrived unexpectedly to examine the plans. He walked heavily round the shed, looked closely at every detail of the plans and snuffed at them once or twice, then stood for a little while contemplating them out of the corner of his eye; then suddenly he lifted his leg, urinated over the plans and walked out without uttering a word.[1]

The whole farm was deeply divided on the subject of the windmill. Snowball did not deny that to build it would be a difficult business. Stone would have to be quarried and built up into walls, then the sails would have to be made and after that there would be need for dynamos and cables. (How these were to be procured, Snowball did not say.) But he maintained that it could all be done in a year. And thereafter, he declared, so much labour would be saved that the animals would only need to work three days a week. Napoleon, on the other hand, argued that the great need of the moment was to increase food production, and that if they wasted time on the windmill they would all starve to death. The animals formed themselves into two factions under the slogan, "Vote for Snowball and the three-day week" and "Vote for Napoleon and the full manger." Benjamin was the only animal who did not side with either faction. He refused to believe either that food would become more plentiful or that the windmill would save work. Windmill or no windmill, he said, life would go on as it had always gone on — that is, badly.

---

1. Character: Napoleon — Rather than fair debate, Napoleon uses unpleasant tactics to try to get his way.

Apart from the disputes over the windmill, there was the question of the defence of the farm. It was fully realised that though the human beings had been defeated in the Battle of the Cowshed they might make another and more determined attempt to recapture the farm and reinstate Mr Jones. They had all the more reason for doing so because the news of their defeat had spread across the countryside and made the animals on the neighbouring farms more restive than ever. As usual, Snowball and Napoleon were in disagreement. According to Napoleon, what the animals must do was to procure firearms and train themselves in the use of them.[1] According to Snowball, they must send out more and more pigeons and stir up rebellion among the animals on the other farms. The one argued that if they could not defend themselves they were bound to be conquered, the other argued that if rebellions happened everywhere they would have no need to defend themselves.[2] The animals listened first to Napoleon, then to Snowball, and could not make up their minds which was right; indeed, they always found themselves in agreement with the one who was speaking at the moment.

At last the day came when Snowball's plans were completed. At the Meeting on the following Sunday the question of whether or not to begin work on the windmill was to be put to the vote. When the animals had assembled in the big barn, Snowball stood up and, though occasionally interrupted by bleating from the sheep, set forth his reasons for advocating the building of the windmill. Then Napoleon stood up to reply. He said very quietly that the windmill was nonsense and that he advised nobody to vote for it, and promptly sat down again; he had spoken for barely thirty seconds, and seemed almost indifferent as to the effect he produced.[3] At this Snowball sprang to his feet, and shouting down the sheep, who had begun bleating again, broke into a passionate appeal in favour of the

---

1. Language & Style — Firearms symbolise violence. Napoleon's desire to use them suggests that he wants or expects violence to play a part in the animals' society.

2. Background & Context — Trotsky wanted to spread revolutionary ideas as far as possible, believing that the support of the international community would be necessary for Russian success. Snowball's plan for defeating the humans mirrors this.

3. Character: Napoleon — This creates tension, as Napoleon's indifference (compared to his strong opposition earlier) hints he might now have another plan to get his way.

windmill. Until now the animals had been about equally divided in their sympathies, but in a moment Snowball's eloquence had carried them away. In glowing sentences he painted a picture of Animal Farm as it might be when sordid labour was lifted from the animals' backs. His imagination had now run far beyond chaff-cutters and turnip-slicers. Electricity, he said, could operate threshing-machines, ploughs, harrows, rollers, and reapers and binders, besides supplying every stall with its own electric light, hot and cold water, and an electric heater. By the time he had finished speaking, there was no doubt as to which way the vote would go. But just at this moment Napoleon stood up and, casting a peculiar sidelong look at Snowball, uttered a high-pitched whimper of a kind no one had ever heard him utter before.

At this there was a terrible baying sound outside, and nine enormous dogs wearing brass-studded collars came bounding into the barn. They dashed straight for Snowball, who only sprang from his place just in time to escape their snapping jaws. In a moment he was out of the door and they were after him. Too amazed and frightened to speak, all the animals crowded through the door to watch the chase. Snowball was racing across the long pasture that led to the road. He was running as only a pig can run, but the dogs were close on his heels. Suddenly he slipped and it seemed certain that they had him. Then he was up again, running faster than ever, then the dogs were gaining on him again. One of them all but closed his jaws on Snowball's tail, but Snowball whisked it free just in time. Then he put on an extra spurt and, with a few inches to spare, slipped through a hole in the hedge and was seen no more.[1]

Silent and terrified, the animals crept back into the barn.[2] In a moment the dogs came bounding back. At first no one had been able to imagine where these creatures came from, but the problem was

---

1. Background & Context — This moment reflects Stalin's rise to power. After years of struggling for control, Stalin exiled his main rival Trotsky in 1929.
2. Characters: The Animals — The animals' reaction to this event contrasts with their jubilation after the Battle of the Cowshed. They don't celebrate Napoleon's actions or Snowball's exile, and their fear suggests they may be concerned that Napoleon's dogs could turn on them, too.

soon solved: they were the puppies whom Napoleon had taken away from their mothers and reared privately. Though not yet full-grown, they were huge dogs, and as fierce-looking as wolves. They kept close to Napoleon. It was noticed that they wagged their tails to him in the same way as the other dogs had been used to do to Mr Jones.[1]

Napoleon, with the dogs following him, now mounted onto the raised portion of the floor where Major had previously stood to deliver his speech. He announced that from now on the Sunday-morning Meetings would come to an end. They were unnecessary, he said, and wasted time. In future all questions relating to the working of the farm would be settled by a special committee of pigs, presided over by himself. These would meet in private and afterwards communicate their decisions to the others. The animals would still assemble on Sunday mornings to salute the flag, sing 'Beasts of England', and receive their orders for the week; but there would be no more debates.[2][3]

In spite of the shock that Snowball's expulsion had given them, the animals were dismayed by this announcement. Several of them would have protested if they could have found the right arguments.[4] Even Boxer was vaguely troubled. He set his ears back, shook his forelock several times, and tried hard to marshal his thoughts; but in the end he could not think of anything to say. Some of the pigs themselves, however, were more articulate. Four young porkers in the front row uttered shrill squeals of disapproval, and all four of them sprang to their feet and began speaking at once. But suddenly the dogs sitting round Napoleon let out deep, menacing growls, and the pigs fell silent and sat down again. Then the sheep broke out into a tremendous bleating of "Four legs good, two legs bad!" which went on for nearly a quarter of an hour and put an end to any chance of discussion.

---

1. Theme: Power — Napoleon is compared to Mr Jones, which suggests he's also corrupt.
2. Key Event — With Snowball gone, Napoleon has taken full control and Animal Farm is no longer a democracy.
3. Theme: Power and Language — Napoleon takes away the animals' freedom of speech. Without this, they have no power.
4. Key Quote — The animals' lack of intelligence means they are unable to speak out against Napoleon.

Afterwards Squealer was sent round the farm to explain the new arrangement to the others.

"Comrades," he said, "I trust that every animal here appreciates the sacrifice that Comrade Napoleon has made in taking this extra labour upon himself. Do not imagine, comrades, that leadership is a pleasure! On the contrary, it is a deep and heavy responsibility.[1] No one believes more firmly than Comrade Napoleon that all animals are equal. He would be only too happy to let you make your decisions for yourselves. But sometimes you might make the wrong decisions, comrades, and then where should we be? Suppose you had decided to follow Snowball, with his moonshine of windmills — Snowball, who, as we now know, was no better than a criminal?"

"He fought bravely at the Battle of the Cowshed," said somebody.

"Bravery is not enough," said Squealer. "Loyalty and obedience are more important. And as to the Battle of the Cowshed, I believe the time will come when we shall find that Snowball's part in it was much exaggerated. Discipline, comrades, iron discipline! That is the watchword for today. One false step, and our enemies would be upon us. Surely, comrades, you do not want Jones back?"

Once again this argument was unanswerable. Certainly the animals did not want Jones back; if the holding of debates on Sunday mornings was liable to bring him back, then the debates must stop. Boxer, who had now had time to think things over, voiced the general feeling by saying: "If Comrade Napoleon says it, it must be right." And from then on he adopted the maxim, "Napoleon is always right[2]," in addition to his private motto of "I will work harder."

By this time the weather had broken and the spring ploughing had begun. The shed where Snowball had drawn his plans of the windmill had been shut up and it was assumed that the plans had been rubbed off the floor. Every Sunday morning at ten o'clock the

---

1. Theme: Propaganda — Squealer's propaganda makes it sound like Napoleon is doing the animals a favour, even though he's taking away their rights and power. This encourages the animals to feel sympathy for Napoleon, instead of anger that their right to debate has been taken away.

2. Key Quote — Boxer spreads propaganda on behalf of the pigs. His lack of education means he doesn't realise he's been brainwashed.

animals assembled in the big barn to receive their orders for the week. The skull of old Major, now clean of flesh, had been disinterred from the orchard and set up on a stump at the foot of the flagstaff, beside the gun.[1] After the hoisting of the flag, the animals were required to file past the skull in a reverent manner before entering the barn. Nowadays they did not sit all together as they had done in the past. Napoleon, with Squealer and another pig named Minimus, who had a remarkable gift for composing songs and poems, sat on the front of the raised platform, with the nine young dogs forming a semicircle round them, and the other pigs sitting behind. The rest of the animals sat facing them in the main body of the barn. Napoleon read out the orders for the week in a gruff soldierly style, and after a single singing of 'Beasts of England' all the animals dispersed.

On the third Sunday after Snowball's expulsion, the animals were somewhat surprised to hear Napoleon announce that the windmill was to be built after all. He did not give any reason for having changed his mind, but merely warned the animals that this extra task would mean very hard work, it might even be necessary to reduce their rations. The plans, however, had all been prepared, down to the last detail. A special committee of pigs had been at work upon them for the past three weeks. The building of the windmill, with various other improvements, was expected to take two years.

That evening Squealer explained privately to the other animals that Napoleon had never in reality been opposed to the windmill. On the contrary, it was he who had advocated it in the beginning, and the plan which Snowball had drawn on the floor of the incubator shed had actually been stolen from among Napoleon's papers. The windmill was, in fact, Napoleon's own creation.[2] Why, then, asked somebody, had he spoken so strongly against it? Here Squealer looked very sly. That, he said, was Comrade Napoleon's cunning. He had *seemed* to oppose the windmill, simply as a manoeuvre

---

1. Background & Context — This reflects how when Lenin died, Stalin put Lenin's body on public display to associate himself with the popular leader.

2. Theme: Propaganda — Squealer takes actual events and finds a way to present them to fit Napoleon's purpose. He doesn't contradict what the animals have seen, which makes his lies more believable.

to get rid of Snowball, who was a dangerous character and a bad influence. Now that Snowball was out of the way, the plan could go forward without his interference. This, said Squealer, was something called tactics. He repeated a number of times, "Tactics, comrades, tactics!" skipping round and whisking his tail with a merry laugh. The animals were not certain what the word meant, but Squealer spoke so persuasively, and the three dogs who happened to be with him[1] growled so threateningly, that they accepted his explanation without further questions.

---

1. Language & Style — This is dramatic irony. The reader knows it's not a coincidence that the dogs are there, and that they've been brought intentionally to intimidate the other animals.

Chapter Six

All that year the animals worked like slaves.[1] But they were happy in their work; they grudged no effort or sacrifice, well aware that everything that they did was for the benefit of themselves and those of their kind who would come after them, and not for a pack of idle, thieving human beings.

Throughout the spring and summer they worked a sixty-hour week, and in August Napoleon announced that there would be work on Sunday afternoons as well. This work was strictly voluntary, but any animal who absented himself from it would have his rations reduced by half.[2] Even so, it was found necessary to leave certain tasks undone. The harvest was a little less successful than in the previous year, and two fields which should have been sown with roots in the early summer were not sown because the ploughing had not been completed early enough. It was possible to foresee that the coming winter would be a hard one.[3]

The windmill presented unexpected difficulties. There was a good quarry of limestone on the farm, and plenty of sand and cement had been found in one of the outhouses, so that all the materials for building were at hand. But the problem the animals could not at first solve was how to break up the stone into pieces of suitable size. There seemed no way of doing this except with picks and crowbars, which no animal could use, because no animal could

---

1. Language & Style — This is ironic. The animals are supposed to be working for their freedom, but they are no better off than "slaves".

2. Theme: Language — Napoleon twists the meaning of "voluntary". Although the work is not technically compulsory, in practice the animals have no choice, because if they don't take part they will go hungry.

3. Theme: Animalism — This harvest is worse than the one in the previous year where the animals worked together. The declining harvest is symbolic of their decline as a society.

stand on his hind legs. Only after weeks of vain effort did the right idea occur to somebody — namely, to utilise the force of gravity. Huge boulders, far too big to be used as they were, were lying all over the bed of the quarry. The animals lashed ropes round these, and then all together, cows, horses, sheep, any animal that could lay hold of the rope — even the pigs sometimes joined in at critical moments — they dragged them with desperate slowness up the slope to the top of the quarry, where they were toppled over the edge, to shatter to pieces below. Transporting the stone when it was once broken was comparatively simple. The horses carried it off in cartloads, the sheep dragged single blocks, even Muriel and Benjamin yoked themselves into an old governess-cart[1] and did their share. By late summer a sufficient store of stone had accumulated, and then the building began, under the superintendence of the pigs.

But it was a slow, laborious process. Frequently it took a whole day of exhausting effort to drag a single boulder to the top of the quarry, and sometimes when it was pushed over the edge it failed to break.[2] Nothing could have been achieved without Boxer, whose strength seemed equal to that of all the rest of the animals put together. When the boulder began to slip and the animals cried out in despair at finding themselves dragged down the hill, it was always Boxer who strained himself against the rope and brought the boulder to a stop. To see him toiling up the slope inch by inch, his breath coming fast, the tips of his hoofs clawing at the ground, and his great sides matted with sweat, filled everyone with admiration. Clover warned him sometimes to be careful not to overstrain himself, but Boxer would never listen to her.[3] His two slogans, "I will work harder" and "Napoleon is always right," seemed to him a sufficient answer to all problems. He had made arrangements with the cockerel to call him three-quarters of an hour earlier in the mornings instead of half

---

1.   governess-cart — a light horse cart usually used to transport people.
2.   Language & Style — Adjectives like "laborious" and "exhausting" show the difficulties the animals face in building the windmill, and their strong determination to finish it.
3.   Character: Boxer — This paragraph strongly highlights Boxer's hardworking nature, but Orwell also creates tension by suggesting something bad may happen if Boxer keeps overworking himself.

an hour. And in his spare moments, of which there were not many nowadays, he would go alone to the quarry, collect a load of broken stone and drag it down to the site of the windmill unassisted.

The animals were not badly off throughout that summer, in spite of the hardness of their work. If they had no more food than they had had in Jones's day, at least they did not have less. The advantage of only having to feed themselves, and not having to support five extravagant human beings as well, was so great that it would have taken a lot of failures to outweigh it. And in many ways the animal method of doing things was more efficient and saved labour. Such jobs as weeding, for instance, could be done with a thoroughness impossible to human beings. And again, since no animal now stole, it was unnecessary to fence off pasture from arable land,[1] which saved a lot of labour on the upkeep of hedges and gates. Nevertheless, as the summer wore on, various unforeseen shortages began to make themselves felt. There was need of paraffin oil, nails, string, dog biscuits and iron for the horses' shoes, none of which could be produced on the farm. Later there would also be need for seeds and artificial manures, besides various tools and, finally, the machinery for the windmill. How these were to be procured, no one was able to imagine.

One Sunday morning, when the animals assembled to receive their orders, Napoleon announced that he had decided upon a new policy. From now onwards Animal Farm would engage in trade with the neighbouring farms: not, of course, for any commercial purpose, but simply in order to obtain certain materials which were urgently necessary.[2] The needs of the windmill must override everything else, he said. He was therefore making arrangements to sell a stack of hay and part of the current year's wheat crop, and later on, if more money were needed, it would have to be made up by the sale of eggs, for which there was always a market in Willingdon. The hens, said Napoleon, should welcome this sacrifice as their own special

---

1.   pasture & arable land — pasture is land where animals graze. Arable land grows food for humans.

2.   Key Event — The pigs interact with humans. This marks the beginning of the boundaries between pigs and humans becoming blurred.

contribution towards the building of the windmill.

Once again the animals were conscious of a vague uneasiness. Never to have any dealings with human beings, never to engage in trade, never to make use of money—had not these been among the earliest resolutions passed at that first triumphant Meeting after Jones was expelled?[1] All the animals remembered passing such resolutions: or at least they thought that they remembered it. The four young pigs who had protested when Napoleon abolished the Meetings raised their voices timidly, but they were promptly silenced by a tremendous growling from the dogs. Then, as usual, the sheep broke into "Four legs good, two legs bad!" and the momentary awkwardness was smoothed over. Finally Napoleon raised his trotter for silence and announced that he had already made all the arrangements. There would be no need for any of the animals to come in contact with human beings, which would clearly be most undesirable. He intended to take the whole burden upon his own shoulders. A Mr Whymper, a solicitor living in Willingdon, had agreed to act as intermediary between Animal Farm and the outside world, and would visit the farm every Monday morning to receive his instructions. Napoleon ended his speech with his usual cry of "Long live Animal Farm!" and after the singing of 'Beasts of England' the animals were dismissed.

Afterwards Squealer made a round of the farm and set the animals' minds at rest. He assured them that the resolution against engaging in trade and using money had never been passed, or even suggested. It was pure imagination, probably traceable in the beginning to lies circulated by Snowball.[2] A few animals still felt faintly doubtful, but Squealer asked them shrewdly, "Are you certain that this is not something that you have dreamed, comrades? Have you any record of such a resolution? Is it written down anywhere?" And since it

---

1. Theme: Animalism — Napoleon goes against one of Old Major's rules, which is not to "engage in trade" with humans.

2. Theme: Propaganda — The pigs start to link anything they see as disagreeable to Snowball, who is now being presented as the enemy of Animal Farm. This brainwashes the animals, because it implies anyone who disagrees with Napoleon (like Snowball did) is evil.

was certainly true that nothing of the kind existed in writing, the animals were satisfied that they had been mistaken.[1]

Every Monday Mr Whymper visited the farm as had been arranged. He was a sly-looking little man with side whiskers, a solicitor in a very small way of business, but sharp enough to have realised earlier than anyone else that Animal Farm would need a broker and that the commissions would be worth having.[2] The animals watched his coming and going with a kind of dread, and avoided him as much as possible. Nevertheless, the sight of Napoleon, on all fours, delivering orders to Whymper, who stood on two legs, roused their pride and partly reconciled them to the new arrangement. Their relations with the human race were now not quite the same as they had been before. The human beings did not hate Animal Farm any less now that it was prospering; indeed, they hated it more than ever. Every human being held it as an article of faith that the farm would go bankrupt sooner or later, and, above all, that the windmill would be a failure.[3] They would meet in the public-houses and prove to one another by means of diagrams that the windmill was bound to fall down, or that if it did stand up, then that it would never work. And yet, against their will, they had developed a certain respect for the efficiency with which the animals were managing their own affairs. One symptom of this was that they had begun to call Animal Farm by its proper name and ceased to pretend that it was called the Manor Farm. They had also dropped their championship of Jones, who had given up hope of getting his farm back and gone to live in another part of the county. Except through Whymper, there was as yet no contact between Animal Farm and the outside world, but there were constant rumours that Napoleon was about to enter into a definite business agreement either with Mr Pilkington of Foxwood or with Mr Frederick of Pinchfield — but never, it was noticed, with

1. Theme: Education — The animals' inability to record events means it's easy for the pigs to manipulate their memories.
2. Character: Mr Whymper — Whymper represents capitalists who were willing to work with the Soviet Union for profit.
3. Background & Context — The windmill represents the Soviet Union's attempts at industrialisation to catch up with the technologies of western countries. The humans' reaction can be seen as the western countries believing the Soviet Union would fail.

both simultaneously.

It was about this time that the pigs suddenly moved into the farmhouse and took up their residence there. Again the animals seemed to remember that a resolution against this had been passed in the early days, and again Squealer was able to convince them that this was not the case. It was absolutely necessary, he said, that the pigs, who were the brains of the farm, should have a quiet place to work in. It was also more suited to the dignity of the Leader (for of late he had taken to speaking of Napoleon under the title of "Leader"[1]) to live in a house than in a mere sty.[2] Nevertheless, some of the animals were disturbed when they heard that the pigs not only took their meals in the kitchen and used the drawing-room as a recreation room, but also slept in the beds. Boxer passed it off as usual with "Napoleon is always right!", but Clover, who thought she remembered a definite ruling against beds, went to the end of the barn and tried to puzzle out the Seven Commandments which were inscribed there. Finding herself unable to read more than individual letters, she fetched Muriel.

"Muriel," she said, "read me the Fourth Commandment. Does it not say something about never sleeping in a bed?"

With some difficulty Muriel spelt it out.

"It says, 'No animal shall sleep in a bed with sheets,'" she announced finally.[3]

Curiously enough, Clover had not remembered that the Fourth Commandment mentioned sheets; but as it was there on the wall, it must have done so. And Squealer, who happened to be passing at this moment, attended by two or three dogs, was able to put the whole matter in its proper perspective.

"You have heard then, comrades," he said, "that we pigs now sleep in the beds of the farmhouse? And why not? You did not suppose, surely, that there was ever a ruling against beds? A bed merely

---

1. Theme: Power & Language — Unlike "Comrade", the title "Leader" sets Napoleon apart as superior to the other animals.
2. Theme: Social Class — The pigs see animal homes as inferior to human homes.
3. Key Event — The pigs tweak the wording of the commandment to fit their needs. The commandments are seen as an "unalterable law" (p.16), so the animals believe them.

means a place to sleep in. A pile of straw in a stall is a bed, properly regarded. The rule was against sheets, which are a human invention. We have removed the sheets from the farmhouse beds, and sleep between blankets.[1] And very comfortable beds they are too! But not more comfortable than we need, I can tell you, comrades, with all the brainwork we have to do nowadays. You would not rob us of our repose, would you, comrades? You would not have us too tired to carry out our duties? Surely none of you wishes to see Jones back?"[2]

The animals reassured him on this point immediately, and no more was said about the pigs sleeping in the farmhouse beds. And when, some days afterwards, it was announced that from now on the pigs would get up an hour later in the mornings than the other animals, no complaint was made about that either.[3]

By the autumn the animals were tired but happy. They had had a hard year, and after the sale of part of the hay and corn, the stores of food for the winter were none too plentiful, but the windmill compensated for everything. It was almost half built now. After the harvest there was a stretch of clear dry weather, and the animals toiled harder than ever, thinking it well worth while to plod to and fro all day with blocks of stone if by doing so they could raise the walls another foot. Boxer would even come out at nights and work for an hour or two on his own by the light of the harvest moon. In their spare moments the animals would walk round and round the half-finished mill, admiring the strength and perpendicularity of its walls and marvelling that they should ever have been able to build anything so imposing. Only old Benjamin refused to grow enthusiastic about the windmill, though, as usual, he would utter nothing beyond the cryptic remark that donkeys live a long time.

November came, with raging south-west winds. Building had to stop because it was now too wet to mix the cement. Finally there came a night when the gale was so violent that the farm buildings

---

1. Language & Style — Squealer's reasoning makes little sense, as blankets are also a human invention. The animals aren't clever enough to notice this, but the reader does.

2. Structure — Squealer's speeches often end with a threat about Jones returning. Squealer does this to capitalise on the animals' greatest fear of Jones returning to the farm.

3. Characters: The Pigs — The pigs are lazy, which contrasts with the animals' hard work.

rocked on their foundations and several tiles were blown off the roof of the barn. The hens woke up squawking with terror because they had all dreamed simultaneously of hearing a gun go off in the distance. In the morning the animals came out of their stalls to find that the flagstaff had been blown down and an elm tree at the foot of the orchard had been plucked up like a radish. They had just noticed this when a cry of despair broke from every animal's throat. A terrible sight had met their eyes. The windmill was in ruins.[1]

With one accord they dashed down to the spot. Napoleon, who seldom moved out of a walk, raced ahead of them all. Yes, there it lay, the fruit of all their struggles, levelled to its foundations, the stones they had broken and carried so laboriously scattered all around. Unable at first to speak, they stood gazing mournfully at the litter of fallen stone. Napoleon paced to and fro in silence, occasionally snuffing at the ground. His tail had grown rigid and twitched sharply from side to side, a sign in him of intense mental activity. Suddenly he halted as though his mind were made up.

"Comrades," he said quietly, "do you know who is responsible for this? Do you know the enemy who has come in the night and overthrown our windmill? SNOWBALL!" he suddenly roared in a voice of thunder. "Snowball has done this thing! In sheer malignity, thinking to set back our plans and avenge himself for his ignominious expulsion, this traitor has crept here under cover of night and destroyed our work of nearly a year. Comrades, here and now I pronounce the death sentence upon Snowball. 'Animal Hero, Second Class,' and half a bushel of apples to any animal who brings him to justice. A full bushel to anyone who captures him alive!"[2]

The animals were shocked beyond measure to learn that even Snowball could be guilty of such an action. There was a cry of indignation, and everyone began thinking out ways of catching Snowball if he should ever come back. Almost immediately the

1. Theme: Animalism — The windmill's destruction reflects how Animalism will never work. Despite how hard the animals have worked, the windmill falls to ruins.
2. Theme: Propaganda — Snowball is made a scapegoat (someone who is blamed for things they haven't done) for Napoleon's failures. This unites the animals against Snowball instead of Napoleon.

footprints of a pig were discovered in the grass at a little distance from the knoll. They could only be traced for a few yards, but appeared to lead to a hole in the hedge. Napoleon snuffed deeply at them and pronounced them to be Snowball's. He gave it as his opinion that Snowball had probably come from the direction of Foxwood Farm.

"No more delays, comrades!" cried Napoleon when the footprints had been examined. "There is work to be done. This very morning we begin rebuilding the windmill, and we will build all through the winter, rain or shine. We will teach this miserable traitor that he cannot undo our work so easily. Remember, comrades, there must be no alteration in our plans: they shall be carried out to the day. Forward, comrades! Long live the windmill! Long live Animal Farm!"[1]

---

1. Character: Napoleon — Napoleon speaks passionately about the windmill because he knows the other animals care about it. He uses their heartbreak over its destruction to strengthen his own support.

Chapter Seven

It was a bitter winter. The stormy weather was followed by sleet and snow, and then by a hard frost which did not break till well into February. The animals carried on as best they could with the rebuilding of the windmill, well knowing that the outside world was watching them and that the envious human beings would rejoice and triumph if the mill were not finished on time.

Out of spite, the human beings pretended not to believe that it was Snowball who had destroyed the windmill:[1] they said that it had fallen down because the walls were too thin. The animals knew that this was not the case. Still, it had been decided to build the walls three feet thick this time instead of eighteen inches as before, which meant collecting much larger quantities of stone. For a long time the quarry was full of snowdrifts and nothing could be done. Some progress was made in the dry frosty weather that followed, but it was cruel work, and the animals could not feel so hopeful about it as they had felt before. They were always cold, and usually hungry as well. Only Boxer and Clover never lost heart. Squealer made excellent speeches on the joy of service and the dignity of labour, but the other animals found more inspiration in Boxer's strength and his never-failing cry of "I will work harder!"

In January food fell short. The corn ration was drastically reduced, and it was announced that an extra potato ration would be issued to make up for it. Then it was discovered that the greater part of the potato crop had been frosted in the clamps, which had not been covered thickly enough. The potatoes had become soft and discoloured, and only a few were edible. For days at a time the animals had nothing to eat but chaff and mangels. Starvation

---

1. Language & Style — As the pigs' lies get more extreme, the narrative voice describing the animals' beliefs becomes more ironic. The reader knows the humans are right.

seemed to stare them in the face.[1]

It was vitally necessary to conceal this fact from the outside world. Emboldened by the collapse of the windmill, the human beings were inventing fresh lies about Animal Farm. Once again it was being put about that all the animals were dying of famine and disease, and that they were continually fighting among themselves and had resorted to cannibalism and infanticide. Napoleon was well aware of the bad results that might follow if the real facts of the food situation were known, and he decided to make use of Mr Whymper to spread a contrary impression. Hitherto the animals had had little or no contact with Whymper on his weekly visits: now, however, a few selected animals, mostly sheep, were instructed to remark casually in his hearing that rations had been increased. In addition, Napoleon ordered the almost empty bins in the store-shed to be filled nearly to the brim with sand, which was then covered up with what remained of the grain and meal. On some suitable pretext Whymper was led through the store-shed and allowed to catch a glimpse of the bins. He was deceived, and continued to report to the outside world that there was no food shortage on Animal Farm.[2]

Nevertheless, towards the end of January it became obvious that it would be necessary to procure some more grain from somewhere. In these days Napoleon rarely appeared in public, but spent all his time in the farmhouse, which was guarded at each door by fierce-looking dogs. When he did emerge, it was in a ceremonial manner, with an escort of six dogs who closely surrounded him and growled if anyone came too near.[3] Frequently he did not even appear on Sunday mornings, but issued his orders through one of the other pigs, usually Squealer.

One Sunday morning Squealer announced that the hens, who had just come in to lay again, must surrender their eggs. Napoleon

---

1.   Background & Context — This food scarcity is similar to the famine in Russia caused by Stalin's agricultural policies.

2.   Theme: Propaganda — Propaganda is used to deceive the humans as well as the animals. This could reflect how Stalin used propaganda to present Russia as a thriving nation to other countries, even when it was struggling.

3.   Character: Napoleon — Napoleon presents himself in a "ceremonial manner". He wants the animals to see him as an untouchable figure, like a god or a king. He no longer pretends that he sees the other animals as his equals.

had accepted, through Whymper, a contract for four hundred eggs a week. The price of these would pay for enough grain and meal to keep the farm going till summer came on and conditions were easier.

When the hens heard this, they raised a terrible outcry. They had been warned earlier that this sacrifice might be necessary, but had not believed that it would really happen. They were just getting their clutches ready for the spring sitting, and they protested that to take the eggs away now was murder. For the first time since the expulsion of Jones, there was something resembling a rebellion. Led by three young Black Minorca pullets, the hens made a determined effort to thwart Napoleon's wishes. Their method was to fly up to the rafters and there lay their eggs, which smashed to pieces on the floor.[1] Napoleon acted swiftly and ruthlessly. He ordered the hens' rations to be stopped, and decreed that any animal giving so much as a grain of corn to a hen should be punished by death. The dogs saw to it that these orders were carried out. For five days the hens held out, then they capitulated and went back to their nesting boxes. Nine hens had died in the meantime. Their bodies were buried in the orchard, and it was given out that they had died of coccidiosis.[2] Whymper heard nothing of this affair, and the eggs were duly delivered, a grocer's van driving up to the farm once a week to take them away.[3]

All this while no more had been seen of Snowball. He was rumoured to be hiding on one of the neighbouring farms, either Foxwood or Pinchfield. Napoleon was by this time on slightly better terms with the other farmers than before. It happened that there was in the yard a pile of timber which had been stacked there ten years earlier when a beech spinney was cleared. It was well seasoned, and Whymper had advised Napoleon to sell it; both Mr Pilkington and Mr Frederick were anxious to buy it. Napoleon was hesitating between the two, unable to make up his mind. It was noticed that

1. Background & Context — The hens' rebellion reflects the peasants' resistance to Stalin's agricultural policy. Many of them burned their crops and killed livestock in protest.
2. coccidiosis — a disease that affects birds.
3. Key Event — This is the closest the animals have come to rebelling against Napoleon so far. It's short-lived though, with the rebellion described in one paragraph. This shows Napoleon's power, as he is able to stop the rebellion quickly and without much fuss.

whenever he seemed on the point of coming to an agreement with Frederick, Snowball was declared to be in hiding at Foxwood, while, when he inclined towards Pilkington, Snowball was said to be at Pinchfield.

Suddenly, early in the spring, an alarming thing was discovered. Snowball was secretly frequenting the farm by night! The animals were so disturbed that they could hardly sleep in their stalls. Every night, it was said, he came creeping in under cover of darkness and performed all kinds of mischief. He stole the corn, he upset the milk-pails, he broke the eggs, he trampled the seed-beds, he gnawed the bark off the fruit trees. Whenever anything went wrong it became usual to attribute it to Snowball. If a window was broken or a drain was blocked up, someone was certain to say that Snowball had come in the night and done it, and when the key of the store-shed was lost, the whole farm was convinced that Snowball had thrown it down the well. Curiously enough, they went on believing this even after the mislaid key was found under a sack of meal.[1] The cows declared unanimously that Snowball crept into their stalls and milked them in their sleep. The rats, which had been troublesome that winter, were also said to be in league with Snowball.

Napoleon decreed that there should be a full investigation into Snowball's activities. With his dogs in attendance he set out and made a careful tour of inspection of the farm buildings, the other animals following at a respectful distance. At every few steps Napoleon stopped and snuffed the ground for traces of Snowball's footsteps, which, he said, he could detect by the smell. He snuffed in every corner, in the barn, in the cowshed, in the hen-houses, in the vegetable garden, and found traces of Snowball almost everywhere. He would put his snout to the ground, give several deep sniffs and exclaim in a terrible voice, "Snowball! He has been here! I can smell him distinctly!" and at the word "Snowball" all the dogs let out blood-curdling growls and showed their side teeth.[2]

The animals were thoroughly frightened. It seemed to them as

---

1. Theme: Propaganda — The propaganda against Snowball is so successful that the animals believe he is responsible for any bad thing, even when it's clearly not him.

2. Background & Context — This mirrors how Stalin invented a conspiracy that people were working with his enemy (the exiled Trotsky) to remove Stalin from power.

though Snowball were some kind of invisible influence, pervading the air about them and menacing them with all kinds of dangers. In the evening Squealer called them together, and with an alarmed expression on his face told them that he had some serious news to report.

"Comrades!" cried Squealer, making little nervous skips, "a most terrible thing has been discovered. Snowball has sold himself to Frederick of Pinchfield Farm, who is even now plotting to attack us and take our farm away from us! Snowball is to act as his guide when the attack begins. But there is worse than that. We had thought that Snowball's rebellion was caused simply by his vanity and ambition. But we were wrong, comrades. Do you know what the real reason was? Snowball was in league with Jones from the very start! He was Jones's secret agent all the time. It has all been proved by documents which he left behind him and which we have only just discovered. To my mind this explains a great deal, comrades. Did we not see for ourselves how he attempted — fortunately without success — to get us defeated and destroyed at the Battle of the Cowshed?"[1]

The animals were stupefied. This was a wickedness far outdoing Snowball's destruction of the windmill. But it was some minutes before they could fully take it in. They all remembered, or thought they remembered, how they had seen Snowball charging ahead of them at the Battle of the Cowshed, how he had rallied and encouraged them at every turn, and how he had not paused for an instant even when the pellets from Jones's gun had wounded his back. At first it was a little difficult to see how this fitted in with his being on Jones's side. Even Boxer, who seldom asked questions, was puzzled. He lay down, tucked his fore hoofs beneath him, shut his eyes, and with a hard effort managed to formulate his thoughts.

"I do not believe that," he said. "Snowball fought bravely at the Battle of the Cowshed. I saw him myself. Did we not give him 'Animal Hero, First Class' immediately afterwards?"

"That was our mistake, comrade. For we know now — it is all written down in the secret documents that we have found — that in reality he was trying to lure us to our doom."

---

1. Structure — Over time, the pigs' propaganda becomes increasingly implausible and further from the truth. This shows their increasing confidence and power.

"But he was wounded," said Boxer. "We all saw him running with blood."

"That was part of the arrangement!" cried Squealer. "Jones's shot only grazed him. I could show you this in his own writing, if you were able to read it.[1] The plot was for Snowball, at the critical moment, to give the signal for flight and leave the field to the enemy. And he very nearly succeeded — I will even say, comrades, he *would* have succeeded if it had not been for our heroic Leader, Comrade Napoleon. Do you not remember how, just at the moment when Jones and his men had got inside the yard, Snowball suddenly turned and fled, and many animals followed him? And do you not remember, too, that it was just at that moment, when panic was spreading and all seemed lost, that Comrade Napoleon sprang forward with a cry of 'Death to Humanity!' and sank his teeth in Jones's leg? Surely you remember *that*, comrades?" exclaimed Squealer, frisking from side to side.

Now when Squealer described the scene so graphically, it seemed to the animals that they did remember it. At any rate, they remembered that at the critical moment of the battle Snowball had turned to flee.[2] But Boxer was still a little uneasy.

"I do not believe that Snowball was a traitor at the beginning," he said finally. "What he has done since is different. But I believe that at the Battle of the Cowshed he was a good comrade."[3]

"Our Leader, Comrade Napoleon," announced Squealer, speaking very slowly and firmly, "has stated categorically — categorically, comrade — that Snowball was Jones's agent from the very beginning — yes, and from long before the Rebellion was ever thought of."

"Ah, that is different!" said Boxer. "If Comrade Napoleon says it, it must be right."

"That is the true spirit, comrade!" cried Squealer, but it was

---

1. Theme: Education — Squealer suggests it's Boxer's fault he doesn't understand because he can't read. He aims to make the less intelligent animals feel stupid and less powerful.

2. Theme: Propaganda — Napoleon's control over the animals is growing. He can change their memories (even of significant events) through propaganda.

3. Character: Boxer — Boxer is the most loyal to Napoleon, so the fact that he begins to doubt what he's being told shows how ridiculous the propaganda has become.

noticed he cast a very ugly look at Boxer with his little twinkling eyes. He turned to go, then paused and added impressively: "I warn every animal on this farm to keep his eyes very wide open. For we have reason to think that some of Snowball's secret agents are lurking among us at this moment!"

Four days later, in the late afternoon, Napoleon ordered all the animals to assemble in the yard. When they were all gathered together, Napoleon emerged from the farmhouse, wearing both his medals (for he had recently awarded himself 'Animal Hero, First Class' and 'Animal Hero, Second Class'[1]), with his nine huge dogs frisking round him and uttering growls that sent shivers down all the animals' spines. They all cowered silently in their places, seeming to know in advance that some terrible thing was about to happen.[2]

Napoleon stood sternly surveying his audience; then he uttered a high-pitched whimper. Immediately the dogs bounded forward, seized four of the pigs by the ear and dragged them, squealing with pain and terror, to Napoleon's feet. The pigs' ears were bleeding, the dogs had tasted blood, and for a few moments they appeared to go quite mad. To the amazement of everybody, three of them flung themselves upon Boxer. Boxer saw them coming and put out his great hoof, caught a dog in mid-air and pinned him to the ground. The dog shrieked for mercy and the other two fled with their tails between their legs. Boxer looked at Napoleon to know whether he should crush the dog to death or let it go. Napoleon appeared to change countenance[3], and sharply ordered Boxer to let the dog go, whereat Boxer lifted his hoof, and the dog slunk away, bruised and howling.[4]

Presently the tumult died down. The four pigs waited, trembling,

---

1. Language & Style — Earlier, the medals are a symbol of achievement for bravery in battle. By awarding them to himself for nothing, Napoleon makes them meaningless.
2. Language & Style — This creates tension, especially after Squealer has just mentioned that there are "secret agents" on the farm.
3. countenance — facial expression.
4. Key Event — Napoleon lets the dog live, which implies he ordered the attack on Boxer and that the dogs weren't attacking of their own accord. This shows Boxer is no longer in Napoleon's favour, which foreshadows his downfall. This event also shows Napoleon's ruthlessness — he will turn on even the most loyal animals as soon as they disagree with him.

with guilt written on every line of their countenances. Napoleon now called upon them to confess their crimes. They were the same four pigs as had protested when Napoleon abolished the Sunday Meetings. Without any further prompting they confessed that they had been secretly in touch with Snowball ever since his expulsion, that they had collaborated with him in destroying the windmill, and that they had entered into an agreement with him to hand over Animal Farm to Mr Frederick. They added that Snowball had privately admitted to them that he had been Jones's secret agent for years past. When they had finished their confession, the dogs promptly tore their throats out, and in a terrible voice Napoleon demanded whether any other animal had anything to confess.

The three hens who had been the ringleaders in the attempted rebellion over the eggs now came forward and stated that Snowball had appeared to them in a dream and incited them to disobey Napoleon's orders. They too were slaughtered. Then a goose came forward and confessed to having secreted six ears of corn during the last year's harvest and eaten them in the night. Then a sheep confessed to having urinated in the drinking pool — urged to do this, so she said, by Snowball — and two other sheep confessed to having murdered an old ram, an especially devoted follower of Napoleon, by chasing him round and round a bonfire when he was suffering from a cough. They were all slain on the spot. And so the tale of confessions and executions went on, until there was a pile of corpses[1] lying before Napoleon's feet and the air was heavy with the smell of blood, which had been unknown there since the expulsion of Jones.[2][3]

When it was all over, the remaining animals, except for the pigs and dogs, crept away in a body. They were shaken and miserable.

---

1. Narrative Style — The narrative is factual and emotionless, describing the slaughtered animals simply as "a pile of corpses". This reflects how heartless Napoleon is and how easy it is for him to kill them.

2. Key Event — This is a shocking moment, as the animals keep confessing despite knowing they'll be killed, showing how brainwashed they are. The suddenness and scale of the killings shows Napoleon's ruthlessness and the cruelty of his regime.

3. Background & Context — Stalin held 'show trials' for people accused of plotting with Trotsky. They were forced by torture to confess to betraying Stalin and were killed. Millions died this way.

They did not know which was more shocking — the treachery of the animals who had leagued themselves with Snowball, or the cruel retribution they had just witnessed. In the old days there had often been scenes of bloodshed equally terrible, but it seemed to all of them that it was far worse now that it was happening among themselves. Since Jones had left the farm, until today, no animal had killed another animal.[1] Not even a rat had been killed. They had made their way onto the little knoll where the half-finished windmill[2] stood, and with one accord they all lay down as though huddling together for warmth — Clover, Muriel, Benjamin, the cows, the sheep and a whole flock of geese and hens — everyone, indeed, except the cat, who had suddenly disappeared just before Napoleon ordered the animals to assemble. For some time nobody spoke. Only Boxer remained on his feet. He fidgeted to and fro, swishing his long black tail against his sides and occasionally uttering a little whinny of surprise. Finally he said:

"I do not understand it. I would not have believed that such things could happen on our farm. It must be due to some fault in ourselves. The solution, as I see it, is to work harder. From now onwards I shall get up a full hour earlier in the mornings."

And he moved off at his lumbering trot and made for the quarry. Having got there, he collected two successive loads of stone and dragged them down to the windmill before retiring for the night.

The animals huddled about Clover, not speaking. The knoll where they were lying gave them a wide prospect across the countryside. Most of Animal Farm was within their view — the long pasture stretching down to the main road, the hayfield, the spinney, the drinking pool, the ploughed fields where the young wheat was thick and green, and the red roofs of the farm buildings with the smoke curling from the chimneys. It was a clear spring evening.[3] The grass and the bursting hedges were gilded by the level rays of

---

1. Theme: Animalism — Napoleon breaks another commandment that "No animal shall kill any other animal."
2. Language & Style — The windmill is a symbol of hope for the future, so the animals flock here to try and find comfort.
3. Structure — In Chapter Two, the animals look out from the knoll at dawn. The shift to evening here is symbolic of the animals' dreams of freedom slipping away.

the sun. Never had the farm — and with a kind of surprise they remembered that it was their own farm, every inch of it their own property — appeared to the animals so desirable a place. As Clover looked down the hillside her eyes filled with tears. If she could have spoken her thoughts, it would have been to say that this was not what they had aimed at when they had set themselves years ago to work for the overthrow of the human race. These scenes of terror and slaughter were not what they had looked forward to on that night when old Major first stirred them to rebellion. If she herself had had any picture of the future, it had been of a society of animals set free from hunger and the whip, all equal, each working according to his capacity, the strong protecting the weak, as she had protected the lost brood of ducklings with her foreleg on the night of Major's speech. Instead — she did not know why — they had come to a time when no one dared speak his mind, when fierce, growling dogs roamed everywhere, and when you had to watch your comrades torn to pieces after confessing to shocking crimes. There was no thought of rebellion or disobedience in her mind.[1] She knew that, even as things were, they were far better off than they had been in the days of Jones, and that before all else it was needful to prevent the return of the human beings. Whatever happened she would remain faithful, work hard, carry out the orders that were given to her, and accept the leadership of Napoleon. But still, it was not for this that she and all the other animals had hoped and toiled. It was not for this that they had built the windmill and faced the pellets of Jones's gun. Such were her thoughts, though she lacked the words to express them.[2]

At last, feeling this to be in some way a substitute for the words she was unable to find, she began to sing 'Beasts of England'. The other animals sitting round her took it up, and they sang it three times over — very tunefully, but slowly and mournfully, in a way they had never sung it before.

They had just finished singing it for the third time when Squealer, attended by two dogs, approached them with the air of having

---

1. Key Quote — Even after seeing her friends killed, Clover still has no intention to rebel. This highlights the extent of the brainwashing the animals have received.

2. Narrative Style — This part of the text uses Clover's perspective to remind the reader of the contrast between Old Major's original vision and Napoleon's cruel dictatorship.

something important to say. He announced that, by a special decree of Comrade Napoleon, 'Beasts of England' had been abolished. From now onwards it was forbidden to sing it.

The animals were taken aback.

"Why?" cried Muriel.

"It is no longer needed, comrade," said Squealer stiffly. "'Beasts of England' was the song of the Rebellion. But the Rebellion is now completed. The execution of the traitors this afternoon was the final act. The enemy both external and internal has been defeated.[1] In 'Beasts of England' we expressed our longing for a better society in days to come. But that society has now been established. Clearly this song has no longer any purpose."[2]

Frightened though they were, some of the animals might possibly have protested, but at this moment the sheep set up their usual bleating of "Four legs good, two legs bad," which went on for several minutes and put an end to the discussion.

So 'Beasts of England' was heard no more. In its place Minimus, the poet, had composed another song which began:

Animal Farm, Animal Farm,
Never through me shalt thou come to harm!

and this was sung every Sunday morning after the hoisting of the flag. But somehow neither the words nor the tune ever seemed to the animals to come up to 'Beasts of England'.

---

1. Language & Style — The "internal" enemies are the "traitors" who have been executed, but this could also refer to any internal thoughts of rebellion in the surviving animals.

2. Theme: Power & Language — The song is about the animals' dream of freedom from work and tyranny. By banning it, Napoleon ensures the song won't be used against him in the future.

Chapter Eight

A few days later, when the terror caused by the executions had died down, some of the animals remembered — or thought they remembered — that the Sixth Commandment decreed: "No animal shall kill any other animal." And though no one cared to mention it in the hearing of the pigs or the dogs, it was felt that the killings which had taken place did not square with this. Clover asked Benjamin to read her the Sixth Commandment, and when Benjamin, as usual, said that he refused to meddle in such matters, she fetched Muriel.[1] Muriel read the Commandment for her. It ran: "No animal shall kill any other animal *without cause.*" Somehow or other, the last two words had slipped out of the animals' memory.[2] But they saw now that the Commandment had not been violated; for clearly there was good reason for killing the traitors who had leagued themselves with Snowball.

Throughout that year the animals worked even harder than they had worked in the previous year. To rebuild the windmill, with walls twice as thick as before, and to finish it by the appointed date, together with the regular work of the farm, was a tremendous labour. There were times when it seemed to the animals that they worked longer hours and fed no better than they had done in Jones's day. On Sunday mornings Squealer, holding down a long strip of paper with his trotter, would read out to them lists of figures proving that the production of every class of foodstuff had increased by two hundred per cent, three hundred per cent, or five hundred per cent, as the case

---

1. Character: Benjamin — Benjamin still refuses to "meddle" in the pigs' oppressive regime, even after seeing fellow animals executed. This shows just how passive he is.
2. Language & Style — There's dramatic irony here. The reader knows the pigs are changing the commandments, but the narrative viewpoint shows that the other animals haven't yet realised this.

might be.[1] The animals saw no reason to disbelieve him, especially as they could no longer remember very clearly what conditions had been like before the Rebellion. All the same, there were days when they felt that they would sooner have had less figures and more food.

All orders were now issued through Squealer or one of the other pigs. Napoleon himself was not seen in public as often as once in a fortnight. When he did appear, he was attended not only by his retinue of dogs but by a black cockerel who marched in front of him and acted as a kind of trumpeter, letting out a loud "cock-a-doodle-doo" before Napoleon spoke. Even in the farmhouse, it was said, Napoleon inhabited separate apartments from the others. He took his meals alone, with two dogs to wait upon him, and always ate from the Crown Derby dinner service which had been in the glass cupboard in the drawing-room.[2] It was also announced that the gun would be fired every year on Napoleon's birthday, as well as on the other two anniversaries.[3]

Napoleon was now never spoken of simply as "Napoleon." He was always referred to in formal style as "our Leader, Comrade Napoleon," and the pigs liked to invent for him such titles as Father of All Animals, Terror of Mankind, Protector of the Sheepfold, Ducklings' Friend, and the like.[4] In his speeches, Squealer would talk with the tears rolling down his cheeks of Napoleon's wisdom, the goodness of his heart, and the deep love he bore to all animals everywhere, even and especially the unhappy animals who still lived in ignorance and slavery on other farms. It had become usual to give Napoleon the credit for every successful achievement and every stroke of good fortune. You would often hear one hen remark to another, "Under the guidance of our Leader, Comrade Napoleon, I have laid five eggs in six days"; or two cows, enjoying a drink at

---

1. Background & Context — In Stalin's Russia, false statistics were frequently given out about productivity to make the country sound successful, much like Squealer's lies here.

2. Character: Napoleon — Napoleon acts more like a human than an animal here, which distances him further from the other animals.

3. Theme: Power — The animals are now encouraged to see Napoleon's birthday as an event that is as significant as the animals' victory over the humans.

4. Background & Context — Stalin also had many titles. For example, he was referred to as 'Father of the Peoples' to present him as a caring, loving leader.

the pool, would exclaim, "Thanks to the leadership of Comrade Napoleon, how excellent this water tastes!"[1] The general feeling on the farm was expressed in a poem entitled 'Comrade Napoleon', which was composed by Minimus and which ran as follows:

Friend of the fatherless!
Fountain of happiness![2]
Lord of the swill-bucket! Oh, how my soul is on
Fire when I gaze at thy
Calm and commanding eye,
Like the sun in the sky,
Comrade Napoleon!

Thou art the giver of
All that thy creatures love,
Full belly twice a day, clean straw to roll upon;
Every beast great or small
Sleeps at peace in his stall,
Thou watchest over all,
Comrade Napoleon!

Had I a sucking-pig,
Ere he had grown as big
Even as a pint bottle or as a rolling-pin,
He should have learned to be
Faithful and true to thee,
Yes, his first squeak should be
"Comrade Napoleon!"[3]

Napoleon approved of this poem and caused it to be inscribed

---

1. Theme: Propaganda — The animals have been influenced into crediting Napoleon for things he has no control over. They are spreading propaganda of their own accord.
2. Language & Style — The use of vague metaphors and clichés reflects Orwell's belief that political language often sounded impressive but had no meaning.
3. Theme: Animalism — The poem presents Napoleon as a supreme leader who is the source of all things good. This contradicts the idea of Animalism, where animals are equal and all contribute to a better society.

on the wall of the big barn, at the opposite end from the Seven Commandments.[1] It was surmounted by a portrait of Napoleon, in profile, executed by Squealer in white paint.

Meanwhile, through the agency of Whymper, Napoleon was engaged in complicated negotiations with Frederick and Pilkington. The pile of timber was still unsold. Of the two, Frederick was the more anxious to get hold of it, but he would not offer a reasonable price. At the same time there were renewed rumours that Frederick and his men were plotting to attack Animal Farm and to destroy the windmill, the building of which had aroused furious jealousy in him. Snowball was known to be still skulking on Pinchfield Farm. In the middle of the summer the animals were alarmed to hear that three hens had come forward and confessed that, inspired by Snowball, they had entered into a plot to murder Napoleon. They were executed immediately, and fresh precautions for Napoleon's safety were taken. Four dogs guarded his bed at night, one at each corner, and a young pig named Pinkeye was given the task of tasting all his food before he ate it, lest it should be poisoned.[2]

At about the same time it was given out that Napoleon had arranged to sell the pile of timber to Mr Pilkington; he was also going to enter into a regular agreement for the exchange of certain products between Animal Farm and Foxwood. The relations between Napoleon and Pilkington, though they were only conducted through Whymper, were now almost friendly. The animals distrusted Pilkington, as a human being, but greatly preferred him to Frederick, whom they both feared and hated. As the summer wore on, and the windmill neared completion, the rumours of an impending treacherous attack grew stronger and stronger. Frederick, it was said, intended to bring against them twenty men all armed with guns, and he had already bribed the magistrates and police, so that if he could once get hold of the title-deeds of Animal Farm they would ask no questions. Moreover, terrible stories were leaking out from Pinchfield about the

---

1. Theme: Propaganda — The poem acts as a visual reminder to the animals of Napoleon's importance. It's as if his glory is just as important as the rules of Animalism.
2. Character: Napoleon — Napoleon might be paranoid that Snowball is trying to kill him, but he may also just be manipulating the animals into fearing for his life.

cruelties that Frederick practised upon his animals. He had flogged an old horse to death, he starved his cows, he had killed a dog by throwing it into the furnace, he amused himself in the evenings by making cocks fight with splinters of razor-blade tied to their spurs.[1] The animals' blood boiled with rage when they heard of these things being done to their comrades, and sometimes they clamoured to be allowed to go out in a body and attack Pinchfield Farm, drive out the humans and set the animals free. But Squealer counselled them to avoid rash actions and trust in Comrade Napoleon's strategy.

Nevertheless, feeling against Frederick continued to run high. One Sunday morning Napoleon appeared in the barn and explained that he had never at any time contemplated selling the pile of timber to Frederick; he considered it beneath his dignity, he said, to have dealings with scoundrels of that description. The pigeons who were still sent out to spread tidings of the Rebellion were forbidden to set foot anywhere on Foxwood, and were also ordered to drop their former slogan of "Death to Humanity" in favour of "Death to Frederick." In the late summer yet another of Snowball's machinations was laid bare. The wheat crop was full of weeds, and it was discovered that on one of his nocturnal visits Snowball had mixed weed seeds with the seed corn. A gander who had been privy to the plot had confessed his guilt to Squealer and immediately committed suicide by swallowing deadly nightshade berries.[2] The animals now also learned that Snowball had never — as many of them had believed hitherto — received the order of 'Animal Hero, First Class.' This was merely a legend which had been spread some time after the Battle of the Cowshed by Snowball himself. So far from being decorated, he had been censured[3] for showing cowardice in the battle.[4] Once again some of the animals heard this with a

---

1. Theme: Propaganda — These rumours are similar to the ones the humans spread about Animal Farm when it was first formed. It hints that the pigs are using the same tactics as the humans and therefore becoming increasingly similar to them.

2. Narrative Voice — The matter-of-fact tone and the lack of reaction from the animals suggests that they are no longer shocked by news of plots or the death of animals.

3. censured — condemned

4. Theme: Propaganda — Propaganda has changed the animals' view of Snowball from a war hero to a coward.

certain bewilderment, but Squealer was soon able to convince them that their memories had been at fault.

In the autumn, by a tremendous, exhausting effort — for the harvest had to be gathered at almost the same time — the windmill was finished. The machinery had still to be installed, and Whymper was negotiating the purchase of it, but the structure was completed. In the teeth of every difficulty, in spite of inexperience, of primitive implements, of bad luck and of Snowball's treachery, the work had been finished punctually to the very day! Tired out but proud, the animals walked round and round their masterpiece, which appeared even more beautiful in their eyes than when it had been built the first time. Moreover, the walls were twice as thick as before. Nothing short of explosives would lay them low this time![1] And when they thought of how they had laboured, what discouragements they had overcome, and the enormous difference that would be made in their lives when the sails were turning and the dynamos running — when they thought of all this, their tiredness forsook them and they gambolled round and round the windmill, uttering cries of triumph.[2] Napoleon himself, attended by his dogs and his cockerel, came down to inspect the completed work; he personally congratulated the animals on their achievement, and announced that the mill would be named Napoleon Mill.

Two days later the animals were called together for a special meeting in the barn. They were struck dumb with surprise when Napoleon announced that he had sold the pile of timber to Frederick.[3] Tomorrow Frederick's wagons would arrive and begin carting it away. Throughout the whole period of his seeming friendship with Pilkington, Napoleon had really been in secret agreement with Frederick.

All relations with Foxwood had been broken off; insulting

---

1. Language & Style — This celebration of the windmill hints at future events, as it reveals that the windmill still has a weakness.

2. Language & Style — Orwell uses a long, complex sentence here with lots of emotive language to reflect how building the windmill has been a long, gruelling process.

3. Background & Context — Napoleon's deal to sell timber to Frederick can be seen as an allegory for the Nazi-Soviet pact, which Russia signed with Hitler's Germany in 1939.

messages had been sent to Pilkington. The pigeons had been told to avoid Pinchfield Farm and to alter their slogan from "Death to Frederick" to "Death to Pilkington." At the same time Napoleon assured the animals that the stories of an impending attack on Animal Farm were completely untrue, and that the tales about Frederick's cruelty to his own animals had been greatly exaggerated. All these rumours had probably originated with Snowball and his agents. It now appeared that Snowball was not, after all, hiding on Pinchfield Farm, and in fact had never been there in his life: he was living — in considerable luxury, so it was said — at Foxwood, and had in reality been a pensioner of Pilkington for years past.[1]

The pigs were in ecstasies over Napoleon's cunning. By seeming to be friendly with Pilkington he had forced Frederick to raise his price by twelve pounds. But the superior quality of Napoleon's mind, said Squealer, was shown in the fact that he trusted nobody, not even Frederick. Frederick had wanted to pay for the timber with something called a cheque, which, it seemed, was a piece of paper with a promise to pay written upon it. But Napoleon was too clever for him. He had demanded payment in real five-pound notes, which were to be handed over before the timber was removed. Already Frederick had paid up; and the sum he had paid was just enough to buy the machinery for the windmill.

Meanwhile the timber was being carted away at high speed. When it was all gone, another special meeting was held in the barn for the animals to inspect Frederick's bank-notes. Smiling beatifically, and wearing both his decorations, Napoleon reposed on a bed of straw on the platform, with the money at his side, neatly piled on a china dish from the farmhouse kitchen.[2] The animals filed slowly past, and each gazed his fill. And Boxer put out his nose to sniff at the bank-notes, and the flimsy white things stirred and rustled in his breath.

Three days later there was a terrible hullabaloo. Whymper, his face deadly pale, came racing up the path on his bicycle, flung it

1. Character: Napoleon — Napoleon is a hypocrite. He presents Snowball living in luxury as a reason for the animals to detest him, but lives in luxury himself.
2. Language & Style — The scene is overly extravagant in order to be satirical. It makes Napoleon and his regime seem absurd.

67

down in the yard and rushed straight into the farmhouse. The next moment a choking roar of rage sounded from Napoleon's apartments. The news of what had happened sped round the farm like wildfire. The bank-notes were forgeries! Frederick had got the timber for nothing![1] [2]

Napoleon called the animals together immediately and in a terrible voice pronounced the death sentence upon Frederick. When captured, he said, Frederick should be boiled alive. At the same time he warned them that after this treacherous deed the worst was to be expected. Frederick and his men might make their long-expected attack at any moment. Sentinels were placed at all the approaches to the farm. In addition, four pigeons were sent to Foxwood with a conciliatory message, which it was hoped might re-establish good relations with Pilkington.

The very next morning the attack came.[3] The animals were at breakfast when the look-outs came racing in with the news that Frederick and his followers had already come through the five-barred gate. Boldly enough the animals sallied forth to meet them, but this time they did not have the easy victory that they had had in the Battle of the Cowshed. There were fifteen men, with half a dozen guns between them, and they opened fire as soon as they got within fifty yards. The animals could not face the terrible explosions and the stinging pellets, and in spite of the efforts of Napoleon and Boxer to rally them, they were soon driven back. A number of them were already wounded. They took refuge in the farm buildings and peeped cautiously out from chinks and knot-holes. The whole of the big pasture, including the windmill, was in the hands of the enemy. For the moment even Napoleon seemed at a loss. He paced up and down without a word, his tail rigid and twitching. Wistful glances

---

1. Theme: Animalism — Old Major's warning that "Man serves the interests of no creature except himself" (p.6) proves to be true.
2. Language & Style — This is ironic. Squealer has just claimed that "Napoleon was too clever" for Frederick (p.67), but it is actually Napoleon who was outsmarted.
3. Background & Context — Frederick's attack on Animal Farm breaks their alliance, reflecting how Hitler and Nazi Germany betrayed their alliance with Russia by invading the country in 1941.

were sent in the direction of Foxwood.[1] If Pilkington and his men would help them, the day might yet be won.[2] But at this moment the four pigeons, who had been sent out on the day before, returned, one of them bearing a scrap of paper from Pilkington. On it was pencilled the words: "Serves you right."

Meanwhile Frederick and his men had halted about the windmill. The animals watched them, and a murmur of dismay went round. Two of the men had produced a crowbar and a sledge hammer. They were going to knock the windmill down.

"Impossible!" cried Napoleon. "We have built the walls far too thick for that. They could not knock it down in a week. Courage, comrades!"

But Benjamin was watching the movements of the men intently. The two with the hammer and the crowbar were drilling a hole near the base of the windmill. Slowly, and with an air almost of amusement, Benjamin nodded his long muzzle.

"I thought so," he said. "Do you not see what they are doing? In another moment they are going to pack blasting powder into that hole."

Terrified, the animals waited. It was impossible now to venture out of the shelter of the buildings. After a few minutes the men were seen to be running in all directions. Then there was a deafening roar. The pigeons swirled into the air, and all the animals, except Napoleon, flung themselves flat on their bellies and hid their faces. When they got up again, a huge cloud of black smoke was hanging where the windmill had been. Slowly the breeze drifted it away. The windmill had ceased to exist!

At this sight the animals' courage returned to them. The fear and despair they had felt a moment earlier were drowned in their rage against this vile, contemptible act. A mighty cry for vengeance went

---

1. Language & Style — Having numerous short sentences in a row here increases the pace of the narrative and makes it sound like the situation is becoming desperate quickly for the animals.

2. Character: Napoleon — Napoleon is not the courageous military leader that Snowball is, and he looks to the humans for help rather than charging bravely into battle himself. It's the first time since he's taken charge that Napoleon has shown weakness.

up, and without waiting for further orders they charged forth in a body and made straight for the enemy.[1] This time they did not heed the cruel pellets that swept over them like hail. It was a savage, bitter battle. The men fired again and again, and, when the animals got to close quarters, lashed out with their sticks and their heavy boots. A cow, three sheep and two geese were killed, and nearly everyone was wounded. Even Napoleon, who was directing operations from the rear, had the tip of his tail chipped by a pellet.[2] But the men did not go unscathed either. Three of them had their heads broken by blows from Boxer's hoofs; another was gored in the belly by a cow's horn; another had his trousers nearly torn off by Jessie and Bluebell. And when the nine dogs of Napoleon's own bodyguard, whom he had instructed to make a detour under cover of the hedge, suddenly appeared on the men's flank, baying ferociously, panic overtook them. They saw that they were in danger of being surrounded. Frederick shouted to his men to get out while the going was good, and the next moment the cowardly enemy was running for dear life. The animals chased them right down to the bottom of the field, and got in some last kicks at them as they forced their way through the thorn hedge.

They had won, but they were weary and bleeding.[3] Slowly they began to limp back towards the farm. The sight of their dead comrades stretched upon the grass moved some of them to tears. And for a little while they halted in sorrowful silence at the place where the windmill had once stood. Yes, it was gone; almost the last trace of their labour was gone! Even the foundations were partially destroyed. And in rebuilding it they could not this time, as before, make use of the fallen stones. This time the stones had vanished too. The force of the explosion had flung them to distances of hundreds

---

1. Theme: Animalism — The animals work together by charging as "a body". The return of a human threat unites the animals for the first time in a long while.
2. Theme: Social Class — The juxtaposition of Napoleon's minor wound with the list of dead animals highlights the inequality between the animals. The lower-class animals are on the frontlines dying while their ruler stays in the rear and barely gets hurt.
3. Background & Context — The result of this battle reflects how Russia managed to defeat Germany, but suffered many deaths and injuries as a result of the fighting.

of yards. It was as though the windmill had never been.[1]

As they approached the farm Squealer, who had unaccountably been absent during the fighting, came skipping towards them, whisking his tail and beaming with satisfaction. And the animals heard, from the direction of the farm buildings, the solemn booming of a gun.

"What is that gun firing for?" said Boxer.

"To celebrate our victory!" cried Squealer.

"What victory?" said Boxer. His knees were bleeding, he had lost a shoe and split his hoof, and a dozen pellets had lodged themselves in his hind leg.[2]

"What victory, comrade? Have we not driven the enemy off our soil — the sacred soil of Animal Farm?"

"But they have destroyed the windmill. And we had worked on it for two years!"

"What matter? We will build another windmill. We will build six windmills if we feel like it. You do not appreciate, comrade, the mighty thing that we have done. The enemy was in occupation of this very ground that we stand upon. And now — thanks to the leadership of Comrade Napoleon — we have won every inch of it back again!"

"Then we have won back what we had before," said Boxer.

"That is our victory," said Squealer.

They limped into the yard. The pellets under the skin of Boxer's leg smarted painfully. He saw ahead of him the heavy labour of rebuilding the windmill from the foundations, and already in imagination he braced himself for the task. But for the first time it occurred to him that he was eleven years old and that perhaps his great muscles were not quite what they had once been.[3]

But when the animals saw the green flag flying, and heard the gun

---

1. Key Event — The complete destruction of the windmill symbolises the end of the animals' hopes for a better life under Animalism.

2. Language & Style — The description of Boxer's injuries highlights his sacrifice and makes Squealer's victorious attitude seem very inappropriate.

3. Character: Boxer — Even Boxer's idealism starts to fade. This indicates how much he cared about the windmill, as its destruction is finally making him question his situation.

firing again — seven times it was fired in all — and heard the speech that Napoleon made, congratulating them on their conduct, it did seem to them after all that they had won a great victory. The animals slain in the battle were given a solemn funeral. Boxer and Clover pulled the wagon which served as a hearse, and Napoleon himself walked at the head of the procession. Two whole days were given over to celebrations. There were songs, speeches and more firing of the gun, and a special gift of an apple was bestowed on every animal, with two ounces of corn for each bird and three biscuits for each dog. It was announced that the battle would be called the Battle of the Windmill, and that Napoleon had created a new decoration, the Order of the Green Banner, which he had conferred upon himself.[1] In the general rejoicings the unfortunate affair of the banknotes was forgotten.

It was a few days later than this that the pigs came upon a case of whisky in the cellars of the farmhouse.[2] It had been overlooked at the time when the house was first occupied. That night there came from the farmhouse the sound of loud singing, in which, to everyone's surprise, the strains of 'Beasts of England' were mixed up. At about half-past nine Napoleon, wearing an old bowler hat of Mr Jones's, was distinctly seen to emerge from the back door, gallop rapidly round the yard and disappear indoors again.[3] But in the morning a deep silence hung over the farmhouse. Not a pig appeared to be stirring. It was nearly nine o'clock when Squealer made his appearance, walking slowly and dejectedly, his eyes dull, his tail hanging limply behind him, and with every appearance of being seriously ill. He called the animals together and told them that he had a terrible piece of news to impart. Comrade Napoleon was dying!

A cry of lamentation went up. Straw was laid down outside the

---

1. Theme: Animalism — The sheep that died in the Battle of the Cowshed got a medal, but now only Napoleon gets an award. The contribution of the other animals isn't seen as important.

2. Theme: Animalism — The pigs start to drink alcohol like Jones used to. In doing so, they're breaking another commandment: "No animal shall drink alcohol."

3. Character: Napoleon — Napoleon's behaviour is becoming increasingly human, as he now starts to wear human clothes.

doors of the farmhouse, and the animals walked on tiptoe. With tears in their eyes they asked one another what they should do if their Leader were taken away from them. A rumour went round that Snowball had after all contrived to introduce poison into Napoleon's food. At eleven o'clock Squealer came out to make another announcement. As his last act upon earth, Comrade Napoleon had pronounced a solemn decree: the drinking of alcohol was to be punished by death.[1]

By the evening, however, Napoleon appeared to be somewhat better, and the following morning Squealer was able to tell them that he was well on the way to recovery. By the evening of that day Napoleon was back at work, and on the next day it was learned that he had instructed Whymper to purchase in Willingdon some booklets on brewing and distilling. A week later Napoleon gave orders that the small paddock beyond the orchard, which it had previously been intended to set aside as a grazing-ground for animals who were past work, was to be ploughed up. It was given out that the pasture was exhausted and needed re-seeding: but it soon became known that Napoleon intended to sow it with barley.[2][3]

About this time there occurred a strange incident which hardly anyone was able to understand. One night at about twelve o'clock there was a loud crash in the yard, and the animals rushed out of their stalls. It was a moonlit night. At the foot of the end wall of the big barn, where the Seven Commandments were written, there lay a ladder broken in two pieces. Squealer, temporarily stunned, was sprawling beside it, and near at hand there lay a lantern, a paintbrush and an overturned pot of white paint. The dogs immediately made a ring round Squealer, and escorted him back to the farmhouse as soon as he was able to walk. None of the animals could form any

---

1. Language & Style — Orwell satirises Napoleon through his dramatic response to his hangover. It creates humour, but also presents a serious message that leaders aren't all-powerful, and have the same weaknesses as anybody else.

2. Theme: Animalism — Retirement was meant to be a benefit of Animalism. The destruction of the paddock hints that the animals may not get this benefit.

3. Theme: Animalism — The paddock will be used for growing barley, which is often used to make whisky or beer, rather than for grazing. This shows that Napoleon is prioritising the pigs' enjoyment over the other animals basic needs, such as food.

idea as to what this meant, except old Benjamin, who nodded his muzzle with a knowing air, and seemed to understand, but would say nothing.[1]

But a few days later Muriel, reading over the Seven Commandments to herself, noticed that there was yet another of them which the animals had remembered wrong. They had thought that the Fifth Commandment was "No animal shall drink alcohol," but there were two words that they had forgotten. Actually the Commandment read: "No animal shall drink alcohol *to excess*."

---

1.   Character: Benjamin — Benjamin's choice not to speak out is frustrating for the reader, as he has the power to help the animals understand their situation, but won't use it.

Chapter Nine

Boxer's split hoof was a long time in healing. They had started the rebuilding of the windmill the day after the victory celebrations were ended. Boxer refused to take even a day off work, and made it a point of honour not to let it be seen that he was in pain. In the evenings he would admit privately to Clover that the hoof troubled him a great deal. Clover treated the hoof with poultices of herbs which she prepared by chewing them, and both she and Benjamin urged Boxer to work less hard. "A horse's lungs do not last for ever," she said to him.[1] But Boxer would not listen. He had, he said, only one real ambition left — to see the windmill well under way before he reached the age for retirement.

At the beginning, when the laws of Animal Farm were first formulated, the retiring age had been fixed for horses and pigs at twelve, for cows at fourteen, for dogs at nine, for sheep at seven, and for hens and geese at five. Liberal old-age pensions had been agreed upon. As yet no animal had actually retired on pension, but of late the subject had been discussed more and more. Now that the small field beyond the orchard had been set aside for barley, it was rumoured that a corner of the large pasture was to be fenced off and turned into a grazing-ground for superannuated[2] animals. For a horse, it was said, the pension would be five pounds of corn a day and, in winter, fifteen pounds of hay, with a carrot or possibly an apple on public holidays. Boxer's twelfth birthday was due in the late summer of the following year.

Meanwhile life was hard. The winter was as cold as the last one

---

1. Characters: Clover & Benjamin — These characters show genuine compassion for Boxer. This contrasts with the pigs' treatment of Boxer later in the chapter.
2. superannuated — retired.

had been, and food was even shorter.[1] Once again all rations were reduced, except those of the pigs and the dogs. A too-rigid equality in rations, Squealer explained, would have been contrary to the principles of Animalism. In any case he had no difficulty in proving to the other animals that they were *not* in reality short of food, whatever the appearances might be. For the time being, certainly, it had been found necessary to make a readjustment of rations (Squealer always spoke of it as a "readjustment," never as a "reduction"), but in comparison with the days of Jones the improvement was enormous. Reading out the figures in a shrill, rapid voice, he proved to them in detail that they had more oats, more hay, more turnips than they had had in Jones's day, that they worked shorter hours, that their drinking water was of better quality, that they lived longer, that a larger proportion of their young ones survived infancy, and that they had more straw in their stalls and suffered less from fleas.[2] The animals believed every word of it. Truth to tell, Jones and all he stood for had almost faded out of their memories. They knew that life nowadays was harsh and bare, that they were often hungry and often cold, and that they were usually working when they were not asleep. But doubtless it had been worse in the old days. They were glad to believe so.[3] Besides, in those days they had been slaves and now they were free, and that made all the difference, as Squealer did not fail to point out.

There were many more mouths to feed now. In the autumn the four sows had all littered about simultaneously, producing thirty-one young pigs between them. The young pigs were piebald[4], and as Napoleon was the only boar on the farm, it was possible to guess at their parentage.[5] It was announced that later, when bricks and timber had been purchased, a schoolroom would be built in the

1. Setting — The chapters toward the end of the book, including this one, are set in harsh winters. This reflects the animals' suffering and the bleak outlook for the future.
2. Language & Style — The list emphasises how many lies the animals have been told.
3. Key Quote — The memory of Jones's rule is so faded that it's hard for the animals to compare to what it's like now, so they just assume things must be better.
4. piebald — having patches of two different colours, normally black and white.
5. Theme: Power — Napoleon being the father of so many pigs almost guarantees that the power on Animal Farm will remain in his family for a long time.

farmhouse garden. For the time being, the young pigs were given their instruction by Napoleon himself in the farmhouse kitchen. They took their exercise in the garden, and were discouraged from playing with the other young animals.[1] About this time, too, it was laid down as a rule that when a pig and any other animal met on the path, the other animal must stand aside: and also that all pigs, of whatever degree, were to have the privilege of wearing green ribbons on their tails on Sundays.[2]

The farm had had a fairly successful year, but was still short of money. There were the bricks, sand and lime for the schoolroom to be purchased, and it would also be necessary to begin saving up again for the machinery for the windmill. Then there were lamp oil and candles for the house, sugar for Napoleon's own table (he forbade this to the other pigs, on the ground that it made them fat), and all the usual replacements such as tools, nails, string, coal, wire, scrap-iron and dog biscuits. A stump of hay and part of the potato crop were sold off, and the contract for eggs was increased to six hundred a week, so that that year the hens barely hatched enough chicks to keep their numbers at the same level.[3] Rations, reduced in December, were reduced again in February, and lanterns in the stalls were forbidden to save oil. But the pigs seemed comfortable enough, and in fact were putting on weight if anything. One afternoon in late February a warm, rich, appetising scent, such as the animals had never smelt before, wafted itself across the yard from the little brew-house, which had been disused in Jones's time, and which stood beyond the kitchen. Someone said it was the smell of cooking barley. The animals sniffed the air hungrily and wondered whether a warm mash was being prepared for their supper. But no warm mash appeared, and on the following Sunday it was announced that from now onwards all barley would be reserved for the pigs. The field

---

1. Theme: Education & Social Class — The young pigs get access to education and are separated from the other animals. This will widen the intelligence gap between the upper and lower classes for the next generation, making control even easier for the pigs.
2. Theme: Social Class — The pigs are openly treated as higher-class animals now.
3. Theme: Power — While the pigs have many newborns, the hens are struggling to increase their numbers. This will lead to a greater proportion of pigs on the farm, meaning control will be easier to maintain.

beyond the orchard had already been sown with barley. And the news soon leaked out that every pig was now receiving a ration of a pint of beer daily, with half a gallon for Napoleon himself, which was always served to him in the Crown Derby soup tureen.[1]

But if there were hardships to be borne, they were partly offset by the fact that life nowadays had a greater dignity than it had had before. There were more songs, more speeches, more processions. Napoleon had commanded that once a week there should be held something called a Spontaneous Demonstration, the object of which was to celebrate the struggles and triumphs of Animal Farm.[2] At the appointed time the animals would leave their work and march round the precincts of the farm in military formation, with the pigs leading, then the horses, then the cows, then the sheep, and then the poultry. The dogs flanked the procession and at the head of all marched Napoleon's black cockerel. Boxer and Clover always carried between them a green banner marked with the hoof and the horn and the caption, "Long live Comrade Napoleon!" Afterwards there were recitations of poems composed in Napoleon's honour, and a speech by Squealer giving particulars of the latest increases in the production of foodstuffs, and on occasion a shot was fired from the gun. The sheep were the greatest devotees of the Spontaneous Demonstrations, and if anyone complained (as a few animals sometimes did, when no pigs or dogs were near) that they wasted time and meant a lot of standing about in the cold, the sheep were sure to silence him with a tremendous bleating of "Four legs good, two legs bad!" But by and large the animals enjoyed these celebrations. They found it comforting to be reminded that, after all, they were truly their own masters and that the work they did was for their own benefit.[3] So that, what with the songs, the processions, Squealer's lists of figures, the thunder of the gun, the crowing of the

---

1. Theme: Propaganda — There is no justification given for the pigs drinking beer. They are so powerful that they no longer feel the need to pretend they're following the rules of Animalism.

2. Theme: Language — The pigs twist language. They call the parades spontaneous but they are organised intentionally to keep the animals happy and glorify Napoleon.

3. Theme: Propaganda — The parades are successful. They make the animals think they are working for their own benefit when it is only the pigs profiting.

cockerel and the fluttering of the flag they were able to forget that their bellies were empty, at least part of the time.

In April, Animal Farm was proclaimed a Republic, and it became necessary to elect a President. There was only one candidate, Napoleon, who was elected unanimously.[1] On the same day it was given out that fresh documents had been discovered which revealed further details about Snowball's complicity with Jones. It now appeared that Snowball had not, as the animals had previously imagined, merely attempted to lose the Battle of the Cowshed by means of a stratagem, but had been openly fighting on Jones's side. In fact, it was he who had actually been the leader of the human forces, and had charged into battle with the words "Long live Humanity!" on his lips. The wounds on Snowball's back, which a few of the animals still remembered to have seen, had been inflicted by Napoleon's teeth.[2]

In the middle of the summer Moses the raven suddenly reappeared on the farm, after an absence of several years. He was quite unchanged, still did no work, and talked in the same strain as ever about Sugarcandy Mountain. He would perch on a stump, flap his black wings, and talk by the hour to anyone who would listen. "Up there, comrades," he would say solemnly, pointing to the sky with his large beak — "up there, just on the other side of that dark cloud that you can see — there it lies, Sugarcandy Mountain, that happy country where we poor animals shall rest for ever from our labours!" He even claimed to have been there on one of his higher flights, and to have seen the everlasting fields of clover and the linseed cake and lump sugar growing on the hedges. Many of the animals believed him. Their lives now, they reasoned, were hungry and laborious; was it not right and just that a better world should exist somewhere else? A thing that was difficult to determine was the attitude of the pigs towards Moses. They all declared contemptuously that his stories

---

1.   Theme: Language — This is another abuse of language. The pigs claim the farm is a Republic, where power is held by the people, but Napoleon has all the control.

2.   Theme: Propaganda — The animals' memories about the events of the Battle of the Cowshed have been changed completely over the course of the novella. This shows how manipulation can happen slowly, and without anyone noticing.

about Sugarcandy Mountain were lies, and yet they allowed him to remain on the farm, not working, with an allowance of a gill of beer a day.[1]

After his hoof had healed up, Boxer worked harder than ever. Indeed, all the animals worked like slaves that year. Apart from the regular work of the farm, and the rebuilding of the windmill, there was the schoolhouse for the young pigs, which was started in March. Sometimes the long hours on insufficient food were hard to bear, but Boxer never faltered. In nothing that he said or did was there any sign that his strength was not what it had been. It was only his appearance that was a little altered; his hide was less shiny than it had used to be, and his great haunches seemed to have shrunken. The others said, "Boxer will pick up when the spring grass comes on"; but the spring grass came and Boxer grew no fatter. Sometimes on the slope leading to the top of the quarry, when he braced his muscles against the weight of some vast boulder, it seemed that nothing kept him on his feet except the will to continue. At such times his lips were seen to form the words, "I will work harder"; he had no voice left. Once again Clover and Benjamin warned him to take care of his health, but Boxer paid no attention. His twelfth birthday was approaching. He did not care what happened so long as a good store of stone was accumulated before he went on pension.[2]

Late one evening in the summer, a sudden rumour ran round the farm that something had happened to Boxer. He had gone out alone to drag a load of stone down to the windmill. And sure enough, the rumour was true. A few minutes later two pigeons came racing in with the news: "Boxer has fallen! He is lying on his side and can't get up!"

About half the animals on the farm rushed out to the knoll where the windmill stood. There lay Boxer, between the shafts of the cart, his neck stretched out, unable even to raise his head. His eyes were

---

1. Character: Moses — The pigs tolerate Moses because his stories about Sugarcandy Mountain keep the animals happy, and distract them from the realities of life.
2. Character: Boxer — Boxer is still naive enough to think Napoleon will let him retire, even though the field for pensioners has been destroyed and no animals have yet retired on the farm. He still believes Napoleon has his best interests at heart.

glazed, his sides matted with sweat. A thin stream of blood had trickled out of his mouth.[1] Clover dropped to her knees at his side.

"Boxer!" she cried, "how are you?"

"It is my lung," said Boxer in a weak voice. "It does not matter. I think you will be able to finish the windmill without me.[2] There is a pretty good store of stone accumulated. I had only another month to go in any case. To tell you the truth, I had been looking forward to my retirement. And perhaps, as Benjamin is growing old too, they will let him retire at the same time and be a companion to me."

"We must get help at once," said Clover. "Run, somebody, and tell Squealer what has happened."

All the other animals immediately raced back to the farmhouse to give Squealer the news. Only Clover remained, and Benjamin, who lay down at Boxer's side, and, without speaking, kept the flies off him with his long tail. After about a quarter of an hour Squealer appeared, full of sympathy and concern. He said that Comrade Napoleon had learned with the very deepest distress of this misfortune to one of the most loyal workers on the farm, and was already making arrangements to send Boxer to be treated in the hospital at Willingdon.[3] The animals felt a little uneasy at this. Except for Mollie and Snowball, no other animal had ever left the farm, and they did not like to think of their sick comrade in the hands of human beings. However, Squealer easily convinced them that the veterinary surgeon in Willingdon could treat Boxer's case more satisfactorily than could be done on the farm. And about half an hour later, when Boxer had somewhat recovered, he was with difficulty got onto his feet, and managed to limp back to his stall, where Clover and Benjamin had prepared a good bed of straw for him.

For the next two days Boxer remained in his stall. The pigs had

---

1. Language & Style — The detailed description here contrasts with the novella's usual detached narrative style. This makes the horrifying image more shocking.

2. Character: Boxer — Boxer thinks his injuries don't matter because the windmill can still be finished without him. He doesn't give a thought to his own wellbeing.

3. Character: Napoleon — Squealer says that Napoleon is distressed, but he doesn't come to check on Boxer himself. This suggests he doesn't really care about Boxer.

sent out a large bottle of pink medicine which they had found in the medicine chest in the bathroom, and Clover administered it to Boxer twice a day after meals. In the evenings she lay in his stall and talked to him, while Benjamin kept the flies off him. Boxer professed not to be sorry for what had happened. If he made a good recovery he might expect to live another three years, and he looked forward to the peaceful days that he would spend in the corner of the big pasture. It would be the first time that he had had leisure to study and improve his mind. He intended, he said, to devote the rest of his life to learning the remaining twenty-two letters of the alphabet.

However, Benjamin and Clover could only be with Boxer after working hours, and it was in the middle of the day when the van came to take him away. The animals were all at work weeding turnips under the supervision of a pig, when they were astonished to see Benjamin come galloping from the direction of the farm buildings, braying at the top of his voice. It was the first time that they had ever seen Benjamin excited — indeed, it was the first time that anyone had ever seen him gallop. "Quick, quick!" he shouted. "Come at once! They're taking Boxer away!" Without waiting for orders from the pig, the animals broke off work and raced back to the farm buildings. Sure enough, there in the yard was a large closed van, drawn by two horses, with lettering on its side and a sly-looking man[1] in a low-crowned bowler hat sitting on the driver's seat. And Boxer's stall was empty.

The animals crowded round the van. "Good-bye, Boxer!" they chorused, "good-bye!"

"Fools! Fools!" shouted Benjamin, prancing round them and stamping the earth with his small hoofs. "Fools! Do you not see what is written on the side of that van?"

That gave the animals pause, and there was a hush. Muriel began to spell out the words. But Benjamin pushed her aside and in the midst of a deadly silence he read:

"'Alfred Simmonds, Horse Slaughterer and Glue Boiler, Willingdon. Dealer in Hides and Bone-Meal. Kennels Supplied.'

---

1. Language & Style — The description of the man is negative, which hints that something is wrong.

Do you not understand what that means? They are taking Boxer to the knacker's!"[1]

A cry of horror burst from all the animals. At this moment the man on the box whipped up his horses and the van moved out of the yard at a smart trot. All the animals followed, crying out at the tops of their voices. Clover forced her way to the front. The van began to gather speed. Clover tried to stir her stout limbs to a gallop, and achieved a canter. "Boxer!" she cried. "Boxer! Boxer! Boxer!" And just at this moment, as though he had heard the uproar outside, Boxer's face, with the white stripe[2] down his nose, appeared at the small window at the back of the van.

"Boxer!" cried Clover in a terrible voice. "Boxer! Get out! Get out quickly! They are taking you to your death!"

All the animals took up the cry of "Get out, Boxer, get out!" But the van was already gathering speed and drawing away from them. It was uncertain whether Boxer had understood what Clover had said. But a moment later his face disappeared from the window and there was the sound of a tremendous drumming of hoofs inside the van. He was trying to kick his way out. The time had been when a few kicks from Boxer's hoofs would have smashed the van to matchwood. But alas! his strength had left him; and in a few moments the sound of drumming hoofs grew fainter and died away.[3] In desperation the animals began appealing to the two horses which drew the van to stop. "Comrades, comrades!" they shouted. "Don't take your own brother to his death!" But the stupid brutes, too ignorant to realise what was happening, merely set back their ears and quickened their pace. Boxer's face did not reappear at the window. Too late, someone thought of racing ahead and shutting the five-barred gate; but in another moment the van was through it and rapidly disappearing

---

1. Character: Benjamin — Benjamin only speaks out against the pigs' actions when he realises that Boxer's life is in immediate danger. It is a turning point for his character, but it comes too late to save his friend. Orwell may have done this to highlight the importance of challenging leaders before they accumulate too much power.

2. Language & Style — White often symbolises innocence, so Boxer's white stripe could highlight that he is an innocent victim.

3. Character: Boxer — Boxer has spent so much of his energy on serving the pigs that he has no energy left to save himself. This makes his fate seem even more tragic.

down the road. Boxer was never seen again.[12]

Three days later it was announced that he had died in the hospital at Willingdon, in spite of receiving every attention a horse could have. Squealer came to announce the news to the others. He had, he said, been present during Boxer's last hours.

"It was the most affecting sight I have ever seen!" said Squealer, lifting his trotter and wiping away a tear. "I was at his bedside at the very last. And at the end, almost too weak to speak, he whispered in my ear that his sole sorrow was to have passed on before the windmill was finished. 'Forward, comrades!' he whispered. 'Forward in the name of the Rebellion. Long live Animal Farm! Long live Comrade Napoleon! Napoleon is always right.' Those were his very last words, comrades."

Here Squealer's demeanour suddenly changed. He fell silent for a moment, and his little eyes darted suspicious glances from side to side before he proceeded.

It had come to his knowledge, he said, that a foolish and wicked rumour had been circulated at the time of Boxer's removal. Some of the animals had noticed that the van which took Boxer away was marked "Horse Slaughterer", and had actually jumped to the conclusion that Boxer was being sent to the knacker's. It was almost unbelievable, said Squealer, that any animal could be so stupid. Surely, he cried indignantly, whisking his tail and skipping from side to side, surely they knew their beloved Leader, Comrade Napoleon, better than that? But the explanation was really very simple. The van had previously been the property of the knacker, and had been bought by the veterinary surgeon, who had not yet painted the old name out. That was how the mistake had arisen.

The animals were enormously relieved to hear this. And when Squealer went on to give further graphic details of Boxer's death-bed, the admirable care he had received and the expensive medicines for

---

1. Structure — Orwell increases the pace in these paragraphs, moving quickly from one small event to the next and building to a dramatic climax.

2. Key Event — Boxer is one of the most loyal animals, yet the pigs sell him to the slaughterhouse as soon as he is unable to work. This emphasises how little the pigs care about the animals, no matter how hardworking or loyal they are.

which Napoleon had paid without a thought as to the cost, their last doubts disappeared and the sorrow that they felt for their comrade's death was tempered by the thought that at least he had died happy.[1]

Napoleon himself appeared at the meeting on the following Sunday morning and pronounced a short oration in Boxer's honour. It had not been possible, he said, to bring back their lamented comrade's remains for interment on the farm, but he had ordered a large wreath to be made from the laurels in the farmhouse garden and sent down to be placed on Boxer's grave. And in a few days' time the pigs intended to hold a memorial banquet in Boxer's honour. Napoleon ended his speech with a reminder of Boxer's two favourite maxims, "I will work harder" and "Comrade Napoleon is always right" — maxims, he said, which every animal would do well to adopt as his own.[2]

On the day appointed for the banquet, a grocer's van drove up from Willingdon and delivered a large wooden crate at the farmhouse. That night there was the sound of uproarious singing, which was followed by what sounded like a violent quarrel and ended at about eleven o'clock with a tremendous crash of glass.[3] No one stirred in the farmhouse before noon on the following day. And the word went round that from somewhere or other the pigs had acquired the money to buy themselves another case of whisky.[4]

---

1. Theme: Propaganda — The animals believe Squealer's lies, possibly because it is easier for them to accept that Boxer died happy than to face the truth.

2. Theme: Propaganda — Napoleon exploits Boxer's death as an opportunity to encourage the other animals to be as obedient and loyal as he was.

3. Structure — History seems to be repeating itself as the pigs show signs of turning on each other, just as Mr Jones and the other humans did to each other.

4. Narrative Style — It's upsetting to read that the money from Boxer's death has been wasted on alcohol for the pigs. The narrative style adds to this by not stating the facts outright. The reader has to figure out what has happened, which makes it seem even more tragic when they work it out.

Chapter Ten

Years passed. The seasons came and went, the short animal lives fled by. A time came when there was no one who remembered the old days before the Rebellion, except Clover, Benjamin, Moses the raven, and a number of the pigs.

Muriel was dead; Bluebell, Jessie and Pincher were dead. Jones too was dead — he had died in an inebriates' home[1] in another part of the county. Snowball was forgotten. Boxer was forgotten, except by the few who had known him. Clover was an old stout mare now, stiff in the joints and with a tendency to rheumy eyes. She was two years past the retiring age, but in fact no animal had ever actually retired. The talk of setting aside a corner of the pasture for superannuated animals had long since been dropped. Napoleon was now a mature boar of twenty-four stone. Squealer was so fat that he could with difficulty see out of his eyes.[2] Only old Benjamin was much the same as ever, except for being a little greyer about the muzzle, and, since Boxer's death, more morose and taciturn[3] than ever.

There were many more creatures on the farm now, though the increase was not so great as had been expected in earlier years. Many animals had been born to whom the Rebellion was only a dim tradition, passed on by word of mouth, and others had been bought who had never heard mention of such a thing before their arrival. The farm possessed three horses now besides Clover. They were fine upstanding beasts, willing workers and good comrades, but very stupid. None of them proved able to learn the alphabet beyond the

---

1. inebriates' home — an institution for alcoholics.
2. Theme: Social Class — While many of the other animals have died or deteriorated, the pigs have gained weight. This shows how the gap between social classes has grown.
3. morose and taciturn — miserable and unwilling to talk to others.

letter B.[1] They accepted everything that they were told about the Rebellion and the principles of Animalism, especially from Clover, for whom they had an almost filial[2] respect; but it was doubtful whether they understood very much of it.

The farm was more prosperous now, and better organised; it had even been enlarged by two fields which had been bought from Mr Pilkington. The windmill had been successfully completed at last, and the farm possessed a threshing machine and a hay elevator of its own, and various new buildings had been added to it. Whymper had bought himself a dogcart. The windmill, however, had not after all been used for generating electrical power. It was used for milling corn, and brought in a handsome money profit.[3] The animals were hard at work building yet another windmill; when that one was finished, so it was said, the dynamos would be installed.[4] But the luxuries of which Snowball had once taught the animals to dream, the stalls with electric light and hot and cold water, and the three-day week, were no longer talked about. Napoleon had denounced such ideas as contrary to the spirit of Animalism. The truest happiness, he said, lay in working hard and living frugally.

Somehow it seemed as though the farm had grown richer without making the animals themselves any richer — except, of course, for the pigs and the dogs. Perhaps this was partly because there were so many pigs and so many dogs. It was not that these creatures did not work, after their fashion. There was, as Squealer was never tired of explaining, endless work in the supervision and organisation of the farm. Much of this work was of a kind that the other animals were too ignorant to understand. For example, Squealer told them that the pigs had to expend enormous labours every day upon mysterious things called "files", "reports", "minutes" and "memoranda". These

---

1. Theme: Education — The new animals are unintelligent, which means they're less likely to realise the pigs are taking advantage of them or challenge their authority.

2. filial — parental.

3. Background & Context — Orwell criticises capitalism here by showing that the hard work of the animals hasn't made their lives easier, but has made the ruling class richer.

4. Narrative Voice — The irony from the narrator here creates a bleak tone. The animals have fallen into the same trap of thinking that if they work hard to build a windmill, they'll be rewarded.

were large sheets of paper which had to be closely covered with writing, and as soon as they were so covered, they were burnt in the furnace. This was of the highest importance for the welfare of the farm, Squealer said. But still, neither pigs nor dogs produced any food by their own labour; and there were very many of them, and their appetites were always good.[1]

As for the others, their life, so far as they knew, was as it had always been. They were generally hungry, they slept on straw, they drank from the pool, they laboured in the fields; in winter they were troubled by the cold, and in summer by the flies. Sometimes the older ones among them racked their dim memories and tried to determine whether in the early days of the Rebellion, when Jones's expulsion was still recent, things had been better or worse than now. They could not remember. There was nothing with which they could compare their present lives: they had nothing to go upon except Squealer's lists of figures, which invariably demonstrated that everything was getting better and better.[2] The animals found the problem insoluble; in any case they had little time for speculating on such things now. Only old Benjamin professed to remember every detail of his long life and to know that things never had been, nor ever could be, much better or much worse — hunger, hardship and disappointment being, so he said, the unalterable law of life.

And yet the animals never gave up hope. More, they never lost, even for an instant, their sense of honour and privilege in being members of Animal Farm. They were still the only farm in the whole country — in all England! — owned and operated by animals. Not one of them, not even the youngest, not even the newcomers who had been brought from farms ten or twenty miles away, ever ceased to marvel at that. And when they heard the gun booming and saw the green flag fluttering at the masthead, their hearts swelled with imperishable pride, and the talk turned always towards the old heroic days, the expulsion of Jones, the writing of the Seven

---

1. Theme: Animalism — The pigs' work seems pointless and doesn't produce food, yet it's hinted that they eat far more than the other animals.
2. Theme: Propaganda — With nothing to compare Squealer's lies to, the animals' situation seems unlikely to ever change for the better.

Commandments, the great battles in which the human invaders had been defeated. None of the old dreams had been abandoned. The Republic of the Animals which Major had foretold, when the green fields of England should be untrodden by human feet, was still believed in. Some day it was coming: it might not be soon, it might not be within the lifetime of any animal now living, but still it was coming.[1] Even the tune of 'Beasts of England' was perhaps hummed secretly here and there: at any rate, it was a fact that every animal on the farm knew it, though no one would have dared to sing it aloud.[2] It might be that their lives were hard and that not all of their hopes had been fulfilled; but they were conscious that they were not as other animals. If they went hungry, it was not from feeding tyrannical human beings; if they worked hard, at least they worked for themselves. No creature among them went upon two legs. No creature called any other creature "Master." All animals were equal.

One day in early summer Squealer ordered the sheep to follow him and led them out to a piece of waste ground at the other end of the farm, which had become overgrown with birch saplings. The sheep spent the whole day there browsing at the leaves under Squealer's supervision. In the evening he returned to the farmhouse himself, but, as it was warm weather, told the sheep to stay where they were. It ended by their remaining there for a whole week, during which time the other animals saw nothing of them. Squealer was with them for the greater part of every day. He was, he said, teaching them to sing a new song, for which privacy was needed.

It was just after the sheep had returned, on a pleasant evening when the animals had finished work and were making their way back to the farm buildings, that the terrified neighing of a horse sounded from the yard. Startled, the animals stopped in their tracks. It was Clover's voice. She neighed again, and all the animals broke into a gallop and rushed into the yard. Then they saw what Clover had seen.

---

1. Theme: Animalism — The animals are so idealistic that they don't realise their dream is impossible to achieve.
2. Language & Style — The song that symbolised animal freedom is still hummed in secret. This gives the reader some hope that Animalism has not been totally suppressed.

It was a pig walking on his hind legs.[1]

Yes, it was Squealer. A little awkwardly, as though not quite used to supporting his considerable bulk in that position, but with perfect balance, he was strolling across the yard. And a moment later, out from the door of the farmhouse came a long file of pigs, all walking on their hind legs. Some did it better than others, one or two were even a trifle unsteady and looked as though they would have liked the support of a stick, but every one of them made his way right round the yard successfully. And finally there was a tremendous baying of dogs and a shrill crowing from the black cockerel, and out came Napoleon himself, majestically upright, casting haughty glances from side to side, and with his dogs gambolling round him.

He carried a whip in his trotter.[2]

There was a deadly silence. Amazed, terrified, huddling together, the animals watched the long line of pigs march slowly round the yard. It was as though the world had turned upside-down. Then there came a moment when the first shock had worn off and when in spite of everything — in spite of their terror of the dogs, and of the habit, developed through long years, of never complaining, never criticising, no matter what happened — they might have uttered some word of protest.[3] But just at that moment, as though at a signal, all the sheep burst out into a tremendous bleating of —

"Four legs good, two legs *better*! Four legs good, two legs *better*! Four legs good, two legs *better*![4]"

It went on for five minutes without stopping. And by the time the sheep had quieted down, the chance to utter any protest had passed, for the pigs had marched back into the farmhouse.

Benjamin felt a nose nuzzling at his shoulder. He looked round.

---

1. Structure — Having this sentence as a separate paragraph highlights the horror that the animals feel at seeing the pigs walking like humans.

2. Language & Style — Napoleon carries a whip, a symbol of animal enslavement.

3. Language & Style — This long sentence creates tension as the reader hopes the animals' horror may spark into rebellion. The reader's hope may be increased by the recent reminder that the animals still remember 'Beasts of England'.

4. Key Quote — Snowball invented the phrase "Four legs good, two legs bad" so the sheep could understand the basic idea behind Animalism. The pigs' new chant reverses this completely — it now promotes the opposite of what Animalism stands for.

It was Clover. Her old eyes looked dimmer than ever. Without saying anything, she tugged gently at his mane and led him round to the end of the big barn, where the Seven Commandments were written. For a minute or two they stood gazing at the tarred wall with its white lettering.

"My sight is failing," she said finally. "Even when I was young I could not have read what was written there. But it appears to me that that wall looks different. Are the Seven Commandments the same as they used to be, Benjamin?"

For once Benjamin consented to break his rule, and he read out to her what was written on the wall. There was nothing there now except a single Commandment. It ran:

ALL ANIMALS ARE EQUAL

BUT SOME ANIMALS ARE MORE EQUAL THAN OTHERS.[1]

After that it did not seem strange when next day the pigs who were supervising the work of the farm all carried whips in their trotters. It did not seem strange to learn that the pigs had bought themselves a wireless set, were arranging to install a telephone, and had taken out subscriptions to 'John Bull', 'Tit-Bits', and the 'Daily Mirror'. It did not seem strange when Napoleon was seen strolling in the farmhouse garden with a pipe in his mouth — no, not even when the pigs took Mr Jones's clothes out of the wardrobes and put them on, Napoleon himself appearing in a black coat, ratcatcher breeches and leather leggings, while his favourite sow appeared in the watered silk dress which Mrs Jones had been used to wear on Sundays.[2]

A week later, in the afternoon, a number of dogcarts drove up to the farm. A deputation of neighbouring farmers had been invited to make a tour of inspection. They were shown all over the farm, and expressed great admiration for everything they saw, especially

---

1. Key Quote — The new commandment doesn't make sense. It shows just how much Napoleon has corrupted language.
2. Key Event — The rebellion has come full circle. The pigs have become like humans in physical appearance and attitude, and the animals have gone back to being oppressed.

GEORGE ORWELL

the windmill. The animals were weeding the turnip field. They
worked diligently, hardly raising their faces from the ground, and
not knowing whether to be more frightened of the pigs or of the
human visitors.[1]

That evening loud laughter and bursts of singing came from the
farmhouse. And suddenly, at the sound of the mingled voices, the
animals were stricken with curiosity. What could be happening in
there, now that for the first time animals and human beings were
meeting on terms of equality? With one accord they began to creep
as quietly as possible into the farmhouse garden.

At the gate they paused, half frightened to go on, but Clover led
the way in. They tiptoed up to the house, and such animals as were
tall enough peered in at the dining-room window. There, round the
long table, sat half a dozen farmers and half a dozen of the more
eminent pigs, Napoleon himself occupying the seat of honour at
the head of the table. The pigs appeared completely at ease in their
chairs.[2] The company had been enjoying a game of cards, but had
broken off for the moment, evidently in order to drink a toast. A
large jug was circulating, and the mugs were being refilled with beer.
No one noticed the wondering faces of the animals that gazed in at
the window.[3]

Mr Pilkington, of Foxwood, had stood up, his mug in his hand.
In a moment, he said, he would ask the present company to drink
a toast. But before doing so, there were a few words that he felt it
incumbent upon him to say.

It was a source of great satisfaction to him, he said — and, he was
sure, to all others present — to feel that a long period of mistrust

---

1. Characters: The Pigs — The animals are finally beginning to see that the pigs are just as
   bad as the humans, but the pigs have too much power to be stopped.
2. Characters: The Pigs — The description of the pigs' relaxed demeanour around the
   humans contrasts with the other animals, who looked down at the ground and were
   frightened. This emphasises that the pigs truly believe they are equal to the humans.
3. Theme: Power — When he first gained control, Napoleon was quick to stamp out any
   challenges to his rule. Now, he doesn't notice the animals at all. This hints that he isn't
   worried about being caught in his corruption, which shows he is secure in his power.

and misunderstanding had now come to an end.[1] There had been a time — not that he, or any of the present company, had shared such sentiments — but there had been a time when the respected proprietors of Animal Farm had been regarded, he would not say with hostility, but perhaps with a certain measure of misgiving, by their human neighbours. Unfortunate incidents had occurred, mistaken ideas had been current. It had been felt that the existence of a farm owned and operated by pigs was somehow abnormal and was liable to have an unsettling effect in the neighbourhood. Too many farmers had assumed, without due enquiry, that on such a farm a spirit of licence and indiscipline would prevail. They had been nervous about the effects upon their own animals, or even upon their human employees. But all such doubts were now dispelled. Today he and his friends had visited Animal Farm and inspected every inch of it with their own eyes, and what did they find? Not only the most up-to-date methods, but a discipline and an orderliness which should be an example to all farmers everywhere. He believed that he was right in saying that the lower animals on Animal Farm did more work and received less food than any animals in the county. Indeed, he and his fellow-visitors today had observed many features which they intended to introduce on their own farms immediately.[2]

He would end his remarks, he said, by emphasising once again the friendly feelings that subsisted, and ought to subsist, between Animal Farm and its neighbours. Between pigs and human beings there was not, and there need not be, any clash of interests whatever. Their struggles and their difficulties were one. Was not the labour problem the same everywhere? Here it became apparent that Mr Pilkington was about to spring some carefully-prepared witticism on the company, but for a moment he was too overcome by amusement to be able to utter it. After much choking, during which his various

---

1. Background & Context — The new friendship between Mr Pilkington and the pigs is an allegory for the alliance that Britain and the USA made with Russia, which began during the Second World War.
2. Theme: Animalism — Snowball wanted the ideas from Animal Farm to spread to other farms. Ironically, this looks like it will happen, but due to Napoleon's corruption, it will end up leading to worse conditions for animals rather than giving them freedom.

chins turned purple, he managed to get it out: "If you have your lower animals to contend with," he said, "we have our lower classes!"[1] This *bon mot*[2] set the table in a roar; and Mr Pilkington once again congratulated the pigs on the low rations, the long working-hours and the general absence of pampering which he had observed on Animal Farm.

And now, he said finally, he would ask the company to rise to their feet and make certain that their glasses were full. "Gentlemen," concluded Mr Pilkington, "gentlemen, I give you a toast: To the prosperity of Animal Farm!"

There was enthusiastic cheering and stamping of feet. Napoleon was so gratified that he left his place and came round the table to clink his mug against Mr Pilkington's before emptying it. When the cheering had died down, Napoleon, who had remained on his feet, intimated that he too had a few words to say.

Like all of Napoleon's speeches, it was short and to the point. He too, he said, was happy that the period of misunderstanding was at an end. For a long time there had been rumours — circulated, he had reason to think, by some malignant enemy — that there was something subversive and even revolutionary in the outlook of himself and his colleagues. They had been credited with attempting to stir up rebellion among the animals on neighbouring farms. Nothing could be further from the truth! Their sole wish, now and in the past, was to live at peace and in normal business relations with their neighbours. This farm which he had the honour to control, he added, was a co-operative enterprise. The title-deeds, which were in his own possession, were owned by the pigs jointly.

He did not believe, he said, that any of the old suspicions still lingered, but certain changes had been made recently in the routine of the farm which should have the effect of promoting confidence still further. Hitherto the animals on the farm had had a rather

---

1.   Character: Mr Pilkington — This comment highlights a similarity between the pigs and the humans, but it also shows that Mr Pilkington still sees animals (including the pigs) as different to him. It hints that, despite his friendliness, he doesn't think humans and pigs are equal.

2.   bon mot — witty comment.

foolish custom of addressing one another as "Comrade." This was to be suppressed. There had also been a very strange custom, whose origin was unknown, of marching every Sunday morning past a boar's skull which was nailed to a post in the garden. This too would be suppressed, and the skull had already been buried.[1] His visitors might have observed, too, the green flag which flew from the masthead. If so, they would perhaps have noted that the white hoof and horn with which it had previously been marked had now been removed.[2] It would be a plain green flag from now onwards.

He had only one criticism, he said, to make of Mr Pilkington's excellent and neighbourly speech. Mr Pilkington had referred throughout to "Animal Farm." He could not of course know — for he, Napoleon, was only now for the first time announcing it — that the name "Animal Farm" had been abolished. Henceforward the farm was to be known as "The Manor Farm" — which, he believed, was its correct and original name.[3]

"Gentlemen," concluded Napoleon, "I will give you the same toast as before, but in a different form. Fill your glasses to the brim. Gentlemen, here is my toast: To the prosperity of The Manor Farm!"

There was the same hearty cheering as before, and the mugs were emptied to the dregs. But as the animals outside gazed at the scene, it seemed to them that some strange thing was happening. What was it that had altered in the faces of the pigs? Clover's old dim eyes flitted from one face to another. Some of them had five chins, some had four, some had three. But what was it that seemed to be melting and changing? Then, the applause having come to an end, the company took up their cards and continued the game that had been interrupted, and the animals crept silently away.

But they had not gone twenty yards when they stopped short.

---

1. Character: Napoleon — Napoleon introduced this custom to gain favour with the animals by associating himself with Old Major. Removing the skull shows that Napoleon now cares more about pleasing Pilkington, and no longer worries about the animals liking him.
2. Language & Style — The hoof and horn on the flag symbolised the working animals. Removing these emphasises that the animals' contribution is no longer acknowledged.
3. Structure — The farm regaining its old name highlights the circular structure of the novella. Things have gone back to how they were at the start under Mr Jones.

An uproar of voices was coming from the farmhouse. They rushed back and looked through the window again. Yes, a violent quarrel was in progress. There were shoutings, bangings on the table, sharp suspicious glances, furious denials. The source of the trouble appeared to be that Napoleon and Mr Pilkington had each played an ace of spades simultaneously.[1]

Twelve voices were shouting in anger, and they were all alike. No question, now, what had happened to the faces of the pigs. The creatures outside looked from pig to man, and from man to pig, and from pig to man again: but already it was impossible to say which was which.[2][3]

November 1943 – February 1944

---

1. Background & Context — The uneasy relationship between Mr Pilkington and Napoleon reflects the tense relationship between the USA and Russia. Not long after *Animal Farm* was published, the countries' alliance ended and the Cold War began.
2. Key Quote — The pigs becoming indistinguishable from the humans shows that life for the animals is no better after the rebellion.
3. Genre — This novella can be described as a beast fable. Most beast fables end with a moral where the animals learn something. However, by the end of *Animal Farm* it's hard to tell if the animals have learnt anything, or whether they even realise that they're back where they started before the rebellion.

Knowledge Organiser — Plot

Chapter One

Old Major tells the animals he wants them to live free of human control.

He says the humans are bad & encourages the animals to rebel.

Chapter Two

Old Major dies & the pigs turn his ideas into Animalism.

The animals rebel against Jones and take over the farm.

The pigs make **commandments for Animalism**.

Chapter Three

The **animals work hard** together to make the farm a success.

The animals try to **learn to read** with varying levels of success.

The pigs admit taking **milk & apples**.

Chapter Four

The humans worry their animals will rebel too, so they attack the farm.

Led by Snowball, **the animals win** the battle.

The Battle of the Cowshed

Chapter Five

Napoleon & Snowball disagree over the windmill.

Napoleon's dogs chase Snowball off the farm.

Chapter Six

The pigs start **changing rules** & **use fear to rule**. Conditions worsen.

Half-built **windmill collapses** during storm — the pigs blame Snowball.

Chapter Seven

The hens rebel but are starved into surrendering.

Animals are forced to confess to working with Snowball & are **killed**.

Chapter Eight

Frederick invades the farm.

The Battle of the Windmill

Animals die & are injured. **The windmill is destroyed**.

Chapter Nine

The pigs enjoy luxuries, but others are starving.

Boxer collapses from overwork & is sold to be slaughtered.

Chapter Ten

Many years have passed:

- **The pigs act like humans.**
- **The animals are oppressed** — just like before rebellion.

KO — Background & Context

Orwell & Writing *Animal Farm*

Orwell was **born in India** in **1903**, then **moved to England** when young.

He **volunteered to fight** against right-wing Nationalists in the Spanish Civil War & worked as a **journalist** during WW2.

He **wrote *Animal Farm*** between **1943-1944**, but struggled to find a publisher as the novella was **critical of Russia**, Britain's ally at the time.

The book was **published** in **1945** — Britain & Russia's alliance was uneasy by then. The book was popular and brought Orwell success.

Russia Before the Revolution

Animal Farm is an allegory for events in Russian history from 1917 to 1943.

History	Allegory
Tsar Nicholas II had ruled Russia since 1894. He was powerful & unpopular.	Mr Jones rules Manor Farm — he controls the animals and is cruel.
Most people were peasants who worked hard but earned little.	The animals work hard, but all the profits go to Mr Jones.
The Bolsheviks, led by Lenin, wanted a revolution against the Tsar.	Old Major wants the animals to rebel against Mr Jones.

Key Members of the Bolshevik Party

Key members of the Bolsheviks represented in the novella:

Lenin — Leader of the Bolshevik party. Promoted communism & wanted to overthrow the Tsar. ⟶ **Old Major** — Leader of animals. Promotes animal equality & wants to overthrow Man.

Trotsky — Lenin's right-hand man & expected successor. A skilled, ruthless army leader. ⟶ **Snowball** — Believes in Old Major's ideals. Strong, ruthless military leader.

Stalin — Powerful, corrupt leader, who ordered executions & whose rule led to famine. ⟶ **Napoleon** — In charge. In league with humans. Executes animals & reduces rations.

The Russian Revolution

History	Allegory

1917 — Russians rioted & the Tsar gave up the throne. Bolsheviks overthrew ruling class and seized power.

The animals rebel & force Mr Jones off the farm.

Bolsheviks become Communist Party & only legal party in Russia.

The pigs take control of running the farm.

1924 — Lenin died. Trotsky & Stalin struggled for power of the party.

Napoleon & Snowball fight over the way the farm should be run.

1929 — Trotsky exiled from Russia & Stalin controlled country.

Napoleon drives Snowball off the farm & takes control.

Russia Under Stalin

Propaganda — Stalin used it to show himself as great leader. He removed Trotsky from history books & altered photos to show himself as Lenin's friend.

> Napoleon displays Old Major's skull to associate himself with Old Major. He spreads propaganda & turns Snowball into an enemy.

The Purges — Enemies of Stalin had 'show trials' & were forced to confess to betraying Stalin. They were shot or sent to labour camps — 10 million died.

> Napoleon holds trials for animals, forces them to confess to working with Snowball & executes them.

Peasants — Forced to share the food they produced with the state. They resisted & Stalin sent troops to attack. In protest, peasants burned crops & killed livestock which led to a famine in the 1930s.

> Napoleon forces hens to give up their eggs to be sold — hens rebel & have their rations reduced. Some starve to death.

Alliances — 1939 pact with Hitler, until he invaded Russia (1941). Then allied with Britain/USA until Cold War.

> Napoleon trades with Frederick, but Frederick pays using forged banknotes & attacks the farm. At the end, Napoleon is friends with Pilkington.

Knowledge Organiser — Key Quotes

"All men are enemies. All animals are comrades."

Chapter One (p.6) — from **Old Major's** speech to the animals.

Summarises the key point of Animalism — humans are the enemy.

It also sets up animals for failure — they don't think animals would betray other animals like the pigs do later.

"Can you not understand that liberty is worth more than ribbons?"

Chapter Two (p.11) — **Snowball** tells Mollie she can't have ribbons due to their association with humans. This makes Mollie unhappy.

This quote is ironic — Mollie is being denied "liberty" to wear ribbons.

Snowball focussed on applying Animalism, not making animals happy.

"Four legs good, two legs bad."

Repeated throughout the novella. First appears in **Chapter Three** (p.22) — **Snowball** simplifies Animalism for less bright animals.

Napoleon teaches the sheep to repeat this maxim — drowns out protest from others.

"The only good human being is a dead one."

Chapter Four (p.29) — **Snowball** after Boxer nearly kills a human.

Snowball is cold-hearted and unemotional here.
Contrasts with Boxer who shows concern for the human.

Links Snowball to Trotsky, who was ruthless, e.g. sent an army to kill many men during a rebellion.

"Several of them would have protested if they could have found the right arguments."

Chapter Five (p.37) — About **the animals** after Napoleon bans Sunday debates.

Shows animals' lack of intelligence — they can't think clearly enough to speak out & so lose power. This is a recurring theme in the novella.

"Napoleon is always right"

Repeated throughout the novella. First appears in **Chapter Five** (p.38)
— **Boxer** says it in response to Napoleon's lie that Snowball is a traitor.

Boxer unintentionally spreads propaganda
— helps Napoleon keep power.

"There was no thought of rebellion or disobedience in her mind."

Chapter Seven (p.59) — About **Clover** after witnessing executions.

The pigs' brainwashing is so powerful that Clover (and others) have no plan to rebel against Napoleon, even after seeing fellow animals killed.

"But doubtless it had been worse in the old days. They were glad to believe so."

Chapter Nine (p.76) — About the harsh conditions on the farm.

Animals don't recall life during Jones's rule — they assume life was worse.

Shows animals have fully absorbed the pigs' propaganda.

"Four legs good, two legs *better*!"

Chapter Ten (p.90) — **Sheep** repeat this when the pigs walk on two legs.

Squealer teaches the sheep this — changes phrase taught by Snowball to a meaning that suits the pigs' needs. Shows propaganda is easy to spread.

"ALL ANIMALS ARE EQUAL BUT SOME ANIMALS ARE MORE EQUAL THAN OTHERS."

Chapter Ten (p.91) — Replaces the seven commandments on the barn wall.

Shows that Animalism has been corrupted & is no longer about equality.

Doesn't make logical sense — reflects the pigs corrupting language.

"The creatures outside looked from pig to man [...] already it was impossible to say which was which."

Chapter Ten (p.96) — The animals watching the pigs & humans play cards.

Shows pigs are as bad as humans — new regime is no better than the old.

Knowledge Organiser — Characters

Napoleon

Fierce boar who becomes the leader of Animal Farm.

Napoleon's desire for power turns him into a corrupt leader.

He is intelligent and cunning, able to manipulate the other animals and build power for himself.

Snowball

Brave, clever pig who leads the animals to victory in the Battle of the Cowshed.

Snowball is idealistic and struggles to engage the other animals.

Napoleon sees Snowball as a threat to his leadership and chases him off the farm.

Squealer

Napoleon's right-hand man.

Squeaker is a very persuasive speaker. He takes charge of propaganda & uses his skills to manipulate the truth.

Old Major

Old boar whose vision of a better future for the animals inspires the rebellion.

Old Major is principled. He lays down clear rules for the other animals to follow.

Benjamin

Cynical donkey.

Benjamin deliberately works no harder than he needs to.

He's intelligent, but chooses not to use his knowledge to stop Napoleon and the pigs' rise to power.

Boxer

Hard-working horse who tries his best for the farm.

Boxer isn't very clever and he trusts Napoleon completely.

His solution to problems on the farm is to work harder.

Mollie

Pretty but vain horse.

Mollie doesn't have much interest in the rebellion.

She's more interested in her ribbons & sugar cubes, which are banned under Animalism.

Clover

Kind, maternal horse.

Clover looks after the other animals on the farm.

She isn't very clever & is a loyal follower of Animalism, so she's manipulated easily by the pigs.

The Humans

Mr Jones — the original owner of the Manor Farm. He is a cruel drunkard who doesn't look after his animals — as a result, they rebel against him and chase him off the farm.

Frederick — the owner of a small, well-kept farm. He is dishonest & is rumoured to treat his animals cruelly.

Pilkington — an old-fashioned farmer. His farm is shabby and neglected.

Whymper — a solicitor who helps Napoleon engage in trade with other humans. He only works with the animals for their money.

Moses

Raven who tells animals about a place called 'Sugarcandy Mountain'. The story gives the animals hope of a better afterlife.

The pigs disagree with Moses, but let him stay on the farm because his story helps distract the animals from their situation.

The Other Animals

The Sheep — a mindless flock who spread propaganda for the pigs.

The Hens — rebel against the pigs, but fail and then become obedient.

Knowledge Organiser — Themes

Animalism

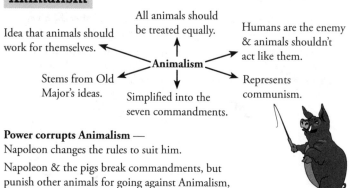

Idea that animals should work for themselves.

All animals should be treated equally.

Humans are the enemy & animals shouldn't act like them.

Animalism

Stems from Old Major's ideas.

Simplified into the seven commandments.

Represents communism.

Power corrupts Animalism —
Napoleon changes the rules to suit him.

Napoleon & the pigs break commandments, but punish other animals for going against Animalism, e.g. the trials & executions in Chapter Seven.

Animalism ultimately fails, as the pigs become similar to the humans & the other animals' lives don't improve. Reflects Orwell's belief that communism in Russia had failed, and Stalin was no better than the Tsar.

Education & Social Class

Education divides animals into social classes:

Ruling Class ⟶ Pigs — smarter & can write, so make the rules. Live in farmhouse & get other animals to step aside.

Working Class ⟶ Other animals — not intelligent, so believe pigs' lies & can't tell that the rules have been changed.

Animals don't make the most of their education & so stay lower class:

*   Mollie only wants to learn to write her name
*   Benjamin refuses to use his reading ability
*   Boxer can only learn four letters

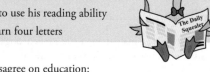

Snowball & Napoleon disagree on education:

Snowball	Napoleon
Wants to educate all animals.	Wants to educate young animals — only puppies (as bodyguards) & pigs.
Wants there to be true equality with all animals understanding Animalism.	Wants pigs to keep power & class system to stay the same.

Power & Language

Power leads to corruption, e.g. the humans & Napoleon.

Napoleon increases his power by controlling:

Actions	Thoughts
Restricting rations & giving the pigs a bigger share	Removing democracy so animals don't have the chance to make decisions themselves
Using dogs to attack his enemies	Using propaganda to make Napoleon seem like a good leader
Having trials & executions to create fear	

Language is also used to control the animals' thoughts:

- The pigs alter the commandments to suit their needs — they tweak the existing wording to mean something new rather than writing new commandments, so the other animals don't realise what's happening.
- Napoleon suppresses freedom of speech — he ends Sunday meetings & banishes Snowball when he disagrees with Napoleon.

The animals are often unable to express their thoughts, which makes them powerless — e.g. they can't find the words to protest when Snowball is exiled.

Propaganda

Propaganda — when a group spreads made-up information to look good.

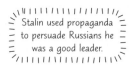

Stalin used propaganda to persuade Russians he was a good leader.

The pigs use propaganda to justify their actions to the other animals. Squealer spreads most of the propaganda and uses it to:

- keep animals loyal — e.g. he talks about animal cruelty on other farms.
- glorify Napoleon — Napoleon gets credit for anything good that happens on the farm.
- blame Snowball — Snowball seen as the enemy, not Napoleon.

The propaganda is so effective, other animals spread it themselves, e.g.

Boxer ⟶ Keeps saying "Napoleon is always right".

Pigeons ⟶ Carry messages like "Death to Humanity" to other farms.

Sheep ⟶ Drown out Napoleon's opposition with their chant.

KO — Writer's Techniques

Structure

Chronological Structure (events told in order) — story easy to follow & lets reader see gradual decline of Animalism.

> ### Events are cyclical
>
> Novella starts & ends with a corrupt leader. Jones is a drunk & Napoleon becomes a drunk too.
>
> The animals are overworked & oppressed under Jones. They then suffer a similar fate under Napoleon.

The ending is **foreshadowed** throughout the text, so the revolution's failure feels inevitable.

E.g. Old Major warns that Jones will sell Boxer to the knacker's yard, which Napoleon ends up doing.

Genre

Allegory

A story that uses characters & events as symbols for something else — this makes things easier to understand than a straightforward political novella.

The novella is an allegory for corrupt communism — mainly Stalin's Soviet Union.

It also comments on corrupt leaders & regimes generally.

Beast Fable

A story that uses animals to teach moral lessons.

Using animals appeals to a wider audience.

Animals are symbols & most aren't fully rounded characters.

Most beast fables end with a clear moral lesson, but in *Animal Farm* the animals learn nothing.

- Jones & Napoleon symbolise all tyrannical dictators — cruel & oppressive.
- Working animals show the inequality in corrupt regimes — the lower classes have no power against their leader.

Narrative Style

The novella uses a **limited narrator** — they only say what the working animals see/hear:

- This viewpoint shows how naive they are, as the reader often understands things that the animals don't.

- Telling the story from the animals' point of view hints that Orwell sympathises with the working class.

The narrative uses **unemotional language** & describes things matter-of-factly. It doesn't **influence** readers — they have to make up their own minds.

Setting

The farm **symbolises Russia** in the early twentieth century.

Jones's farmhouse represents the palaces of wealthy Russians.

Working animals live in **poor conditions** which represent the peasants' situation.

The farm itself is generic & unremarkable — Orwell is suggesting that the novella's events could happen anywhere.

Early chapters are generally set in **summer**, reflecting the animals' initial optimism. Later chapters are in **winter** — this shows the optimism has faded.

Satire & Irony

Irony means saying one thing & meaning another:

- The novella's subtitle is 'A Fairy Story'. This is ironic — fairy stories usually have happy endings, but the animals' story ends badly.

- Squealer's language is often ironic — e.g. "you do not imagine, I hope, that we pigs are doing this in the spirit of selfishness." Shows how words can lose their meaning.

Dramatic irony is when the reader knows something characters don't. It emphasises the animals' ignorance of how badly the pigs are behaving:

- The pigs begin to resemble humans — reader sees this before the animals do.

- The pigs pretend not to break rules by changing the commandments — reader recalls the original commandments, but the animals don't.

Satire makes fun of people or ideas. It's often funny, but makes a serious point.

Novella mocks the Soviet Union — makes their actions seem ridiculous to make a political point.

Having the leaders as pigs makes them seem absurd.

Makes workers seem foolish by comparing them to sheep.

Satire

Criticisms can seem less preachy when using satire.

GEORGE ORWELL

How Characters Speak

Uneducated characters use repetitive language — shows
how easily they are manipulated by slogans and propaganda:

Boxer ⟶ Repeats "Napoleon is always right"
— can't think for himself.

Sheep ⟶ Repeat "Four legs good, two legs bad" —
manipulated by pigs to drown out any disagreements.

Powerful characters use persuasive language to influence other animals:

Old Major ⟶ Political & rhetorical language — animals listen.

Snowball ⟶ Emotional language — skilled speaker,
makes him a threat to Napoleon.

Squealer ⟶ Very persuasive — distorts facts, history & twists words.

Napoleon ⟶ Isn't a good public speaker to start, but over time begins
to use persuasive techniques to manipulate the animals.

Symbolism

Symbol	What it represents	How it changes
Beasts of England	"stirring" song symbolises revolution & hope for the future.	Banned by Napoleon to remove this hope.
Guns & Whip	Violence, control and animal oppression.	Held by pigs instead of humans.
Windmill	Hope that life can improve.	Destroyed — shows impossibility of this hope.
Animalism Flag	Similar to Soviet Union flag. Green — "green fields". Hoof & horn — unity of animals.	Hoof & horn removed — shows working animals no longer have any power.

Rituals that symbolise achievement become worthless by the end:

- **Medals** — originally for all animals, but later Napoleon
awards them to himself for doing nothing.

- **Firing gun** — originally celebrates the animals' victory in battle,
but later used to celebrate Napoleon's birthday.

Discussion Questions

1. How does Napoleon's leadership in the novella
    mirror Stalin's leadership in Russia?
    Pick out some events from the text that support your points.

2. Do you think Snowball was an effective leader? Explain your answer.

3. Does Orwell create sympathy for the animals on the farm?
    How does he achieve this?

4. Do you think the sheep are important characters? Why or why not?

5. Do you think Napoleon would have been able to lead
    effectively without Squealer? Explain your answer.

6. How does Orwell use Animalism to criticise Communism?

7. 'The most important moment for the pigs was teaching themselves to
    read before the other animals.' Do you agree? Explain your opinion.

8. Do you think the animals were ever all truly
    united and equal? Why or why not?

9. How does Orwell show the power of language in the novella?

10. Why do you think Orwell used a cyclical structure in the novella?

11. Do you think the use of allegory in the novella is effective in showing
    Orwell's concerns about corrupt leaders? Explain your answer.

12. How would you describe the narrative style in the novella?
    Why do you think Orwell chose to use this style of narrative?

13. What symbolism does Orwell use in the novella? How
    does the meaning of these symbols change over time?

14. Why do you think Orwell chose to use the setting he did for
    Animal Farm? Think about what it shows and symbolises.

15. The novella ends with the pigs and the humans arguing over a card
    game. Why do you think Orwell chose to end the novella in this way?

GEORGE ORWELL

THE SEVEN COMMANDMENTS
1. Whatever goes upon two legs is an enemy.
2. Whatever goes upon four legs, or has wings, is a freind.
3. No animal shall wear clothes.
4. No animal shall sleep in a bed.
5. No animal shall drink alcohol.
6. No animal shall kill any other animal.
7. All animals are equal.

110

GEORGE ORWELL

EPA41